THE LICHEN SYMBIOSIS

Parmelia enteromorpha. Naturally-occurring thallus with large, brown fruits (apothecia). (2/3 of natural size)

A BLAISDELL BOOK IN THE PURE AND APPLIED SCIENCES

CONSULTING EDITOR

Paul R. Gross, *Massachusetts Institute of Technology*

The
Lichen
Symbiosis

Vernon Ahmadjian

Clark University

BLAISDELL PUBLISHING COMPANY
A Division of Ginn and Company
WALTHAM, MASSACHUSETTS · TORONTO · LONDON

Preface

Lichens are the most striking examples of symbiosis. These associations have been recognized for one hundred years, but their functional relationships are still obscure. The experimental aspects of lichenology have lagged far behind the purely descriptive studies. Two factors are responsible for this: first, the difficulty in culturing lichens and the separate symbionts and second, the scattered information which is available in this area.

The intention of this book is to serve as a guide to the literature, methodology, and present status of experimental lichenology. Hopefully, it will serve also as a stimulus to promote further experimental studies of the lichen symbiosis. The morphology and taxonomy of lichens—areas not covered in this book—and a detailed description of lichen chemistry can be found in Hale's *Lichen Handbook* [114]. A detailed treatment of lichen ecology is given by Barkman [32].

I thank the following individuals who have guided or stimulated me in my study of lichens: Dr. Grace E. Howard, who helped remove some of the frustrations I felt as an undergraduate student trying to identify the lichens of Worcester County, Massachusetts; Dr. David Potter, who first gave me the opportunity to study these associations; Dr. Rolf Santesson, who gave me insight into the taxonomy and ecology of lichens; Dr. I. Mackenzie Lamb, whose patience, guidance, and interest have been a constant source of stimulation; and my wife, June, for her continued patience and assistance.

Worcester, Massachusetts VERNON AHMADJIAN

Contents

3

Physiology of Lichen Symbionts   37

Algal Symbiont

Cultural methods · Nutrition · Growth rate · Factors influencing growth · Lichen substances · Physiological strains · Extracellular products and permeability · Resistance to environmental extremes

Fungal Symbiont

Cultural methods · Nutrition · Growth rate · Factors influencing growth · Lichen substances · Genetic studies

4

Nature of the Lichen Association   63

Origin of lichens · Physical nature of the lichen symbiosis · Lichenlike associations · Physiology of the lichen symbiosis · Specificity of the algal symbiont · Synthesis experiments

5

Physiology of the Composite Plant   89

Growth · Culture · Photosynthesis · Respiration · Water relations · Substrate · Absorption and metabolism · Resistance to environmental extremes

6

Lichen Chemistry   113

1 ❧ Introduction

Lichens have been studied for over two hundred years, yet the basic nature of this type of fungal-algal symbiosis* still remains, to a great extent, a mystery. Lichens are unusual associations. They are distinct morphological entities, easily recognized and classified into separate groups. However, when their individual components are separated and grown in laboratory cultures, each has its own characteristics and does not resemble the *composite plant* which it helps to form under natural conditions [10, 152, 153]. When we consider one lichen, we seem to be dealing with three plants: a fungus, an alga, and the composite form (Figure 1).

A lichen is not a simple mixture of an alga and a fungus. A mushroom covered with or growing among green algae should not be termed a lichen even though its hyphae may be associated intimately with the algal cells and a mutualistic relationship can be demonstrated. There are many examples of naturally occurring fungal-algal associations which may be lichen-like in some respects but are not lichens [58, 143, 196, 207]. A lichen represents not only a physiological interplay between fungus and alga, but the association also results in a new morphological entity, caused largely by a differentiation of the fungus when it unites with an alga.

---

* Symbiosis is defined as a close, long-lasting association of dissimilar organisms. Mutualism is a type of symbiosis where, as with many lichens, both organisms benefit from the association.

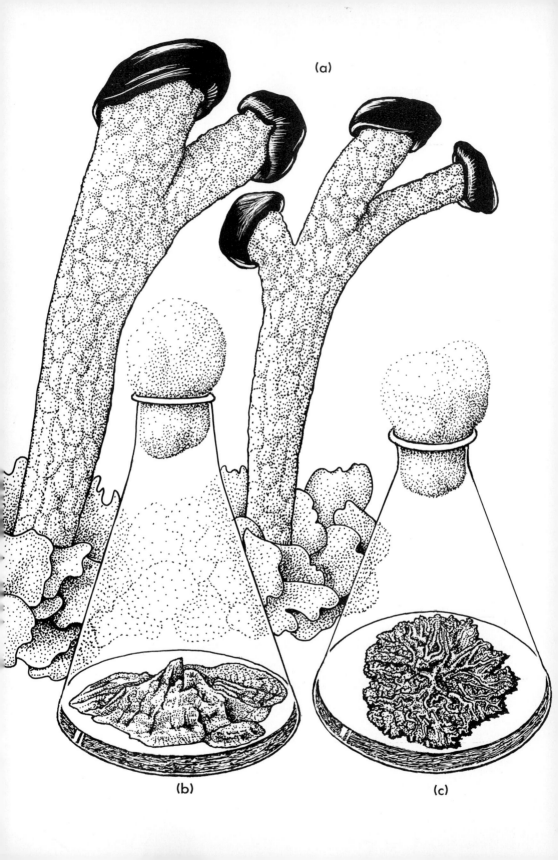

(a)

(b)

(c)

Description and classification of lichens began long before their symbiotic nature was discovered [250], and even now most studies are concerned with morphological and taxonomical aspects of the *composite plant* [66]. Comparatively little attention has been given to the individual components, mainly because of the difficulties and time involved in their separation and growth. Although a *composite plant* is different from either of its isolated components, taxonomically, only the fungus and alga are recognized [114]. Lichens should be regarded only as a biological group, not as a separate systematic class [223, 224].

The fungus is the dominant member of the partnership and determines the morphology of the lichen. Moreover, it produces fruiting bodies which are important criteria for identification. For these reasons, a lichen name refers only to the fungal component, whether it is in association with an alga, which has its own Latin name, or alone in pure culture.

Historical Background

Numerous early workers noted a similarity between the green cells found within the thalli or bodies of lichens and free-living algae. Despite this recognition, these colored cells were thought to be reproductive bodies of the fungus and were called *gonidia.* The free-living algal forms which resembled these green cells were considered to be *gonidia* which had escaped from thalli and were living independently.

A Swiss botanist, Schwendener, after ten years of detailed studies of the anatomy and development of lichens, publicly asserted in 1867 [233] that lichens were not independent plants but associations of fungi and algae. He amplified and defended his views in subsequent publications [234, 235].

As expressed by Schwendener, "As the result of my researches, the lichens are not simple plants, not individuals in the ordinary sense of the word; they are, rather, colonies, which consist of hundreds of thousands of individuals, of which, however, one alone plays the master, while the rest in perpetual captivity prepare the nutriment for themselves and their master. This master is a fungus of the class *Ascomycetes*, a parasite which is accustomed to live upon others' work. Its slaves are green algae, which it has sought out, or indeed caught hold of, and compelled into its service. It

FIGURE 1. (opposite) *Cladonia cristatella:* (a) *composite plant;* (b) fungal symbiont in culture; (c) algal symbiont in culture.

surrounds them, as a spider its prey, with a fibrous net of narrow meshes, which is gradually converted into an impenetrable covering; but while the spider sucks its prey and leaves it dead, the fungus incites the algae found in its net to more rapid activity, even to more vigorous increase . . ."

Schwendener's theory resulted in a bitter controversy [63, 64]. The prominent lichen systematists of that time, who assailed both the theory and its author, found it difficult to adjust their established concept of a lichen as an individual plant to one that viewed these forms as a combination of two dissimilar organisms. Nor could they understand how these plants, which were long-lived and of healthy appearance, could be the results of parasitic relationships. Schwendener's announcement also initiated a series of investigations which were designed to prove or disprove his theory by separation and attempted resynthesis of the two components. The basic technique used in these studies was to sow spores from a fungal component onto cultures of its algal symbiont or similar free-living algae. These early experiments were not completely successful, but they did reveal the initial stages of synthesis: namely, intimate contacts between fungal germ tubes and algal cells and verification experimentally of the composite nature of lichens. Today there is no doubt of the genetic independence of the fungal and algal components of lichens.

Present Areas of Study

At present, investigations on lichens are being conducted over a broad front, although lichenologists are still a rare breed in comparison to the number of workers in most other areas of biological study. Taxonomical investigations, especially detailed monographic treatments of various genera, and morphological studies have a major emphasis in lichenological research. Artificial and traditional groupings are being replaced by more inclusive and natural assemblages. Ecological, environmental, and chemical variants are now recognized in attempts toward natural systems of classification [272, 294]. One goal in lichen taxonomy is to incorporate the lichen fungi into the general mycological system [114, 224].

Much work has been done on lichen chemistry [27, 245]. Recent studies have been concerned with the isolation, identification, biosynthesis, and biological effects of lichen substances. Hale [114] has estimated that approximately one half of the known lichens in temperate regions will inhibit bacterial growth and that in most cases the active principle can be traced to a specific chemical compound. Recent experiments [16] have tried to induce production of these compounds by the isolated fungal components because at present it is impossible to grow the *composite plants* in a laboratory for long periods of time in order to obtain large quantities of their antibiotic substances.

The physiology and biochemistry of the *composite plants* and their isolated components have received increased attention in recent years. Studies of the growth, nutrition, and metabolism of these organisms have contributed much to our understanding of the functional aspects of lichen symbioses.

Ecological and developmental studies, especially with regard to microclimate [32], and studies of the effects of radiation [47] and environmental extremes have been conducted on a number of lichens. However, more detailed and quantitative information is needed on the wide variety of groups in order to obtain a clearer and more accurate picture of their natural behavior.

Electron microscopy studies of lichens have been difficult to conduct, due perhaps to the friable nature of these associations or to the different preparative treatment which each symbiont requires. The few studies which exist provide some information on the physical relationships between the symbionts, but cellular details are lacking [13, 38, 183].

With regard to the genetic and sexual mechanisms of lichen fungi there is little definitive information. This area of lichenology has proved to be the most baffling and challenging.

Guide to the Literature

Recent reviews on lichens include several on the biology of the symbiosis by Quispel [210], Smith [255, 256], Schaede [225], Steiner [263], Haynes [120], and Ahmadjian [12, 13], one on anatomy and morphology by Ozenda [194], on taxonomy by Weber [294] and Thomson [272], on chemistry by Shibata [244, 245], and on ecology by Barkman [32]. An outstanding general review is by Des Abbayes [75], who has also compiled listings of published papers on different aspects of lichenology from 1939 to 1952 [76]. Llano [169, 170] has published detailed reviews on the economic uses of lichens.

Several older works must be mentioned because of their importance as guides to early literature. A classic book by Smith [250] contains detailed treatments of most aspects of lichenology. Tobler's two books [274, 275] are concerned with the developmental and functional aspects of the lichen symbiosis.

Lists of recent publications on all aspects of lichenology are published by Culberson in each issue of *The Bryologist,* which is a quarterly journal of the American Bryological Society.

For a general review of symbiotic associations, see Henry [131].

Isolation and Nature
2 ❧ of Lichen Symbionts

ALGAL SYMBIONT

Isolation Techniques

Isolation of an algal component, or phycobiont [237], of a lichen can be accomplished by several methods. Regardless of the technique used, one must be certain that the alga which is isolated is the true phycobiont. A lichen thallus is a good substrate for foreign algae which generally grow faster than the lichenized forms.

The simplest method of isolating a phycobiont is to inoculate small fragments of a washed lichen thallus into an illuminated mineral solution (Appendix). With foliose or leaflike forms (Figure 2), the upper layer or cortex is scraped away and pieces of the underlying algal layer used for inoculum. Although both partners are placed into one medium, the phycobiont will outgrow its heterotrophic fungal partner within two to three weeks and develop in a free-living condition. Microscopic comparison must be made of the separated alga with phycobiont cells within the thallus, since it is likely that foreign algae will also develop in the culture. Subsequent transfers of the cultured phycobiont will result in a unialgal culture.

Early investigators placed thin slices of a lichen into an illuminated

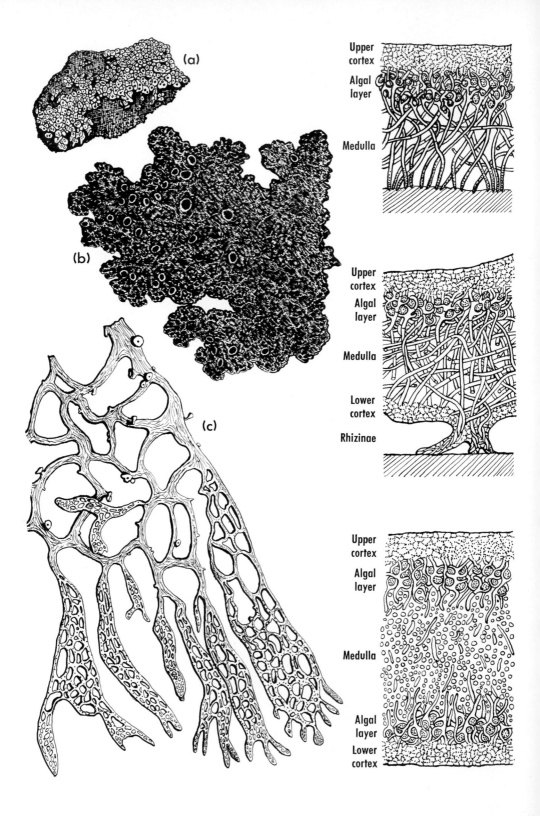

Upper cortex

Algal layer

Medulla

Upper cortex

Algal layer

Medulla

Lower cortex

Rhizinae

Upper cortex

Algal layer

Medulla

Algal layer

Lower cortex

(a)

(b)

(c)

axenic = pure culture

damp chamber and waited for the moisture and light conditions to cause outgrowths of the algal symbiont and disintegration of the fungal tissue. They identified cells of the true algal partner by means of the hyphal fragments which adhered to their walls. These methods are suitable for obtaining generic identifications of phycobionts, but for other studies they have several disadvantages. First, the algal cultures obtained are not bacteria-free and cannot be used for axenic (= pure) culture investigations. Second, a culture is derived from many cells which may be of different genetic types—a factor which would influence the results of nutritional and physiological studies. Unsuccessful attempts have been made to soak thalli in 2 M KCl or MgSO$_4$ solutions, in order to plasmolyze any epiphytes on the thallus surface [44].

The best isolation method involves use of a micropipette. This method is difficult to master and is time consuming, but it avoids the problems of other procedures. With a micropipette one can obtain uncontaminated colonies, each derived from a single cell, with regularity and be assured that the organisms isolated are true algal symbionts. The procedure is as follows: All glassware and necessary equipment are sterilized. Micropipettes are pulled from 3–4 mm glass tubes (nine inch segments plugged with cotton at both ends) and examined under a microscope to determine whether or not the openings are large enough and the pipette tips too jagged. In general, the opening of a micropipette should be approximately 50–75 microns in diameter. This small bore is obtained first by drawing the glass tube into two gross pipettes using a regular bunsen burner flame. The micropipette is drawn by grasping the gross pipette with a forceps, gently heating the glass over a small flame (obtained by connecting the gas supply tube to a segment of glass tubing which is tapered at one end) until it softens and then in an action which should occur simultaneously with removal of the pipette from the flame, stretching the softened glass with a rapid, smooth pull [203]. By means of fine forceps, the sealed end of the micropipette is removed with a sharp pull.

A thallus is washed with cold tap water for about fifteen minutes to remove extraneous material. If the specimens are fragile, they can be sewed

FIGURE 2. (opposite) Lichens are of three major types. Crustose lichens (a) adhere closely to their substratum. The foliose type (b) is leafy in form and is attached to its substratum more loosely. Fruticose lichens are either pendulous strands (c) or hollow, upright stalks. The diagrams at right show vertical sections of crustose and foliose lichen thalli and a horizontal section of a fruticose thallus.

to an index card and this card then tacked onto a board which is placed under the tap. With foliose lichens, portions of the upper cortex are scraped away with a scalpel and bits of the algal layer are taken. With crustose, or crustlike forms, and fruticose, or stalked forms, the cleanest parts of a thallus are selected. Small bits of a thallus are placed in a drop of distilled water on a glass plate. By means of a glass slide, which is pressed over the fragments and rubbed gently in a circular motion, the pieces are broken up until a green suspension results. The suspension is poured into a glass vial and kept as stock material. Microscopic examination of a drop of this suspension will show numerous free-lying algal cells surrounded by broken pieces of fungal hyphae. Many algal cells will retain bits of hyphae on their walls. This type of cell (Figure 3) must be

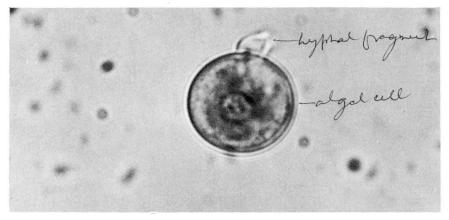

FIGURE 3. Algal cell (*Trebouxia*) from a fragmented thallus of *Xanthoria parietina*. The algal cell has a hyphal fragment attached to its wall. This is the type of cell that is selected in micropipette isolations of the algal symbiont of lichens. (2000 x)

selected because it represents the true algal symbiont. The small hyphal fragments usually do not develop in culture. After an algal cell of this type has been chosen, it is transferred by a micropipette through four or five successive water drops, or until the cell is clear from surrounding visible impurities. The objective of the microscope should be of a size which will allow enough working distance between the objective lens and the glass slide and yet contribute to produce sufficient magnification (total of about 100x). A length of rubber tubing added to the glass pipette will facilitate transfers of the cell. With the rubber tube firmly positioned in his mouth, the worker need not depend on capillary action but can apply suction to free a cell which adheres to the glass slide. By forcing air through the pipette, which is placed next to a cell, he also can blow the cell free if need be. Moreover, because of the added length which this tubing gives to the micropipette, the worker is able to place a transferred cell in the area of the water drop that is in the microscope's field of vision. This saves him the time of trying to find anew the cell in each successive drop. Also, he can regulate the amount of water and possible contaminants transferred with an algal cell by pulling out the micropipette from the water drop as soon as he sees the desired cell emerge. Sometimes, when the algal cell is introduced into a new drop of water it floats on the surface. It is impossible to suck up the cell in this position with a micropipette. Generally, most cells will sink after a few minutes. Before the last two transfers of an algal cell, the micropipette tip is steamed, an action which may reduce contamination of the cultures. This can be achieved by holding the tip of the pipette for a few seconds in front of a jet of steam (obtained by boiling water in a flask capped with a stopper through which a bent glass tube, tapered at the outer end, passes). After the cells are transferred through the water drops, they are inoculated into test tubes which contain a solid nutrient medium (agar slants) (Appendix). The micropipette is pulled gently along the surface of the agar slant while the worker blows out the one-cell suspension from the pipette. Small air bubbles emerging from the tip of the pipette will signal the end of the transfer.

An average of fifteen single-cell isolates should be made for each lichen species. The cultures will develop best at a cool (15–20C) temperature either under illuminated conditions (50–100 ft.c.) or in complete darkness. Most green algal symbionts can grow saprophytically. Depending on the species of algal symbiont, colonies become visible from two to six weeks. The percentage of colonies obtained will vary greatly. With proper use of this isolation technique there should not be much contamination.

The isolation of phycobionts which are filamentous in the free-living state but separated into single cells in the lichenized state, into bacteria-free cultures presents another problem. The best approach is to place small fragments of lichens that contain these phycobionts into illuminated mineral water solutions and wait for the algae to grow out from within the fungal tissue. Individual algal filaments may be isolated with a micropipette. To obtain axenic cultures of blue-green phycobionts the investigator must eliminate the bacteria that are present within gelatinous sheaths which envelop the algal cells. One method is to irradiate the algal cells with ultraviolet light at an intensity sufficient to destroy the bacteria but not the algae [124].   Another method is to use broad spectrum antibiotics [292].

Classification and Description

Twenty-six genera of algae have been found in lichen associations (Table 1) [15]. Eight genera are of blue-green algae, seventeen genera are of green algae, and one genus is of a yellow-green alga. Among the greens, species of *Trebouxia,* a unicellular alga, are the most common. In fact, the majority of described lichens have *Trebouxia* as phycobionts. *Coccomyxa and Trentepohlia* are also common green phycobionts. *Trentepohlia* and *Phycopeltis* are prevalent in tropical lichens. Among the blue-greens *Nostoc and Scytonema* are the most common phycobionts [1, 15] (Figure 4). A rough estimate of the geographical frequency of phycobionts is that in tropical regions about 5–10% of all lichen species have blue-green phycobionts, while the rest have phycobionts equally divided among the *Trentepohliaceae* (*Trentepohlia, Phycopeltis, Cephaleuros*) and other green algae. In temperate regions about 8% of the lichen species have blue-green algae as phycobionts, about 9% have members of

TABLE 1

Algal Genera That Participate as Primary Symbionts in Lichen Associations
After Ahmadjian, 1966 [15].

Algal Genera[1]	*Lichen Associations* (*Genera*)
I. Chlorophyceae (Grass-green algae)	
A. Chlorococcales	
1. Chlorella	Calicium, Lecidea, Lepraria
2. Gloeocystis	Gyalecta
3. Myrmecia	Bacidia, Catillaria, Dermatocarpon, Lecidea, Maronella, Psoroma, Sarcogyne, Verrucaria
4. Pseudochlorella	Lecidea
5. Trebouxia	Alectoria, Buellia Caloplaca, Cetraria, Cladonia, Lecanora, Lecidea, Parmelia, Physcia, Ramalina, Stereocaulon, Umbilicaria, Xanthoria
6. Trochiscia	Polyblastia

[1] Taxonomic arrangement according to G. M. Smith, *The Fresh-Water Algae of the United States* (New York: McGraw-Hill, 1950), 719 pp., as modified by W. Herndon, "Studies on Chlorosphaeracean Algae from Soil," *Am. J. Botany, 45* (1958), 298–308.

26 genera .

Algal Genera	Lichen Associations (Genera)
B. Chlorosphaerales	
1. Chlorosarcina	Lecidea
2. Coccomyxa	Icmadophila, Peltigera, Solorina
3. Hyalococcus	Dermatocarpon
C. Ulotrichales	
1. Cephaleuros	Raciborskiella, Strigula (foliicolous lichens)
2. Coccobotrys	Lecidea, Verrucaria
3. Leptosira	Thrombium
4. Phycopeltis	Arthonia, Mazosia, Opegrapha, Porina, Trichothelium (foliicolous lichens)
5. Pleurococcus	Endocarpon, Lecidea, Staurothele, Thelidium Verrucaria
6. Pseudopleurococcus	Verrucaria
7. Stichococcus	Calicium, Chaenotheca, Coniocybe, Lepraria
8. Trentepohlia	Arthonia, Chaenotheca, Graphis, Gyalecta, Opegrapha, Pyrenula (Very common symbiont of tropical and sub-tropical lichens)

II. Cyanophyceae (Blue-green algae)
  A. Chamaesiphonales
    1. Hyella — Arthopyrenia
  B. Chroococcales
    1. Chroococcus ✓ — Phylliscum, Pyrenopsidium
    2. Gloeocapsa ✓ — Peccania, Psorotichia, Pyrenopsis, Synalissa

  C. Oscillatoriales
    1. Calothrix — Calotrichopsis, Lichina, Porocyphus
    2. Dichothrix — Placynthium
    3. Nostoc ✓ — Collema, Hydrothyria, Leptogium, Pannaria, Peltigera
    4. Scytonema ✓ — Coccocarpia, Erioderma, Heppia, Lichenothrix, Lichinodium, Pannaria, Polychidium, Thermutis, Zahlbrucknerella
    5. Stigonema ✓ — Ephebe, Spilonema

III. Xanthophyceae (Yellow-green algae)
  A. Heterotrichales
    1. Heterococcus (=Monocilia) — Verrucaria

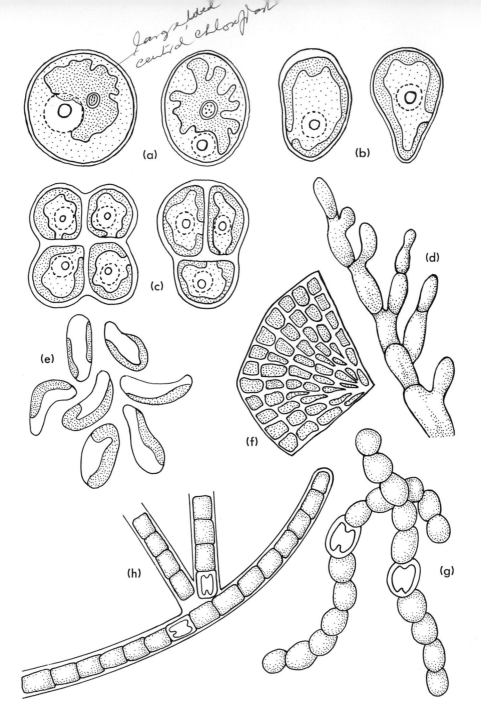

tangential
central chloroplast

FIGURE 4. The most common types of algae found in lichen associations: (a) *Trebouxia*; (b) *Myrmecia*; (c) *Pleurococcus*; (d) *Trentepohlia*; (e) *Coccomyxa*; (f) *Phycopeltis*; (g) *Nostoc*; (h) *Scytonema*. After Anne S. Beard.

the *Trentepohliaceae*, and about 83% have other genera of green algae [223].

The modifications which algae undergo within a lichen thallus are varied. In species of *Collema* the *Nostoc* phycobionts retain their filamentous nature. In other lichens their filaments are broken up completely and each individual cell is encased within fungal tissue. The filamentous nature of blue-green phycobionts such as *Calothrix* and *Scytonema* is not evident in many lichen thalli and this makes *in situ* identification impossible. However, once free of the restraining influence of the fungus, the alga will produce the same filaments which it would normally form in a free-living state (Figure 5). Some single-celled algae can be identified while they are within a thallus. For example, *Trebouxia* cells are recognized easily by their large central chloroplasts and prominent central pyrenoids (Figure 6). One diagnostic trait for algal identification—namely,

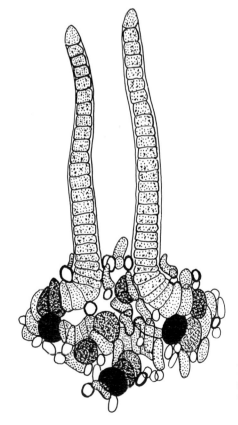

FIGURE 5. A phycobiont assuming its free-living filamentous form after becoming free of the fungal hyphae.

zoospore production—cannot be used since the algae do not produce zoo-spores when they are part of a lichen [3]. Modifications which affect the normal pigmentation of an alga also occur. In the free-living state *Trentepohlia* forms beta-carotene in such abundance that structural details of its cells are completely obscured. In a lichenized state, however, its cells are almost entirely free from pigmentation. *Gloeocapsa* has gelatinous sheaths that are pigmented in the free-living condition but faintly colored or even colorless in a lichenized state [75]. Two conjectures can be made to explain this absence of pigment. Either the demand for organic compounds by the fungus on its algal partner is so great as to interfere with the normal metabolic processes involved in pigment formation or the fungus exerts an inhibitory action on its algal partner's capacity for pigment synthesis.

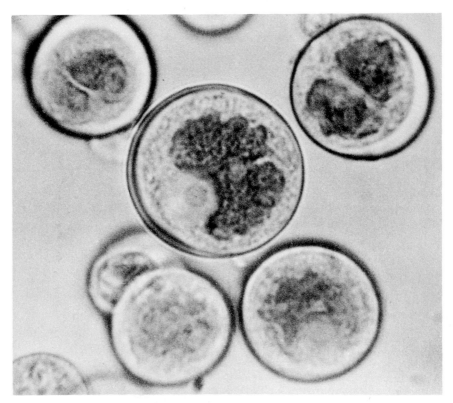

FIGURE 6. *Trebouxia* from *Candelaria concolor* v. *antarctica*. Cell in the center of the photograph shows central chloroplast and pyrenoid, parietal nucleus and nucleolus. (2000 x)

The first conjecture seems more probable because free-living algae in mineral solutions show a marked reduction in pigmentation.

Some lichens have algal cells within their fruiting tissues. The algae usually are unicellular forms and are called either hymenial or epithecial algae, depending on their location within the fruiting body. In some instances, the hymenial algae are of a different genus than the primary phycobiont of the thallus. For example, in *Staurothele catalepta Stichococcus* is the hymenial alga while *Pleurococcus* is the thallus alga [16]. In cases where both algae are similar, cells of the hymenial and epithecial algae are much smaller than their counterparts in the thallus [304]. It was thought earlier that their smaller size was due to a mechanical pressure from the reproductive tissue that surrounded them. However, this does not explain why epithecial algae, which are attached very loosely near the surface of a fruiting body, also are small. The influence of a chemical agent secreted by the fruits has been suggested as another explanation for these size differences. The hymenial and epithecial algae are carried along with the discharged fungal spores and help to hasten the development of new lichen individuals.

Cultural Characteristics

The algal symbionts of many lichens have been isolated and cultured. In many cases the phycobionts were of species which are found in free-living conditions [15]. For example, from two specimens of *Lichina confinis*, a marine lichen collected in Norway and Spain, the blue-green alga *Calothrix pulvinata* was isolated and identified as phycobiont. This alga is a common, free-living organism in the same general habitat as the lichen. Another specimen of *L. confinis* collected in Sweden had *Calothrix crustacea*, another common, free-living alga, as phycobiont [9]. However, *Trebouxia*, which is the most common algal symbiont in lichens, is rarely, if ever, encountered in a free-living state [5, 15].

Trebouxia cells grown on organic nutrient agar differ from those within a lichen. The cells are larger and assume shapes which are more pronounced than in a lichen thallus. The forty or more described species of *Trebouxia* fall clearly into two groups [2, 6]. The first group (Figure 7) has ellipsoidal or oval cells (Figure 8) and each cell has a deeply incised and lobed chloroplast. When a cell divides, its chloroplast cleaves successively into equal segments which then assume positions against the cell wall (Figure 9). The second group (Figure 10) has spherical cells

Marine lichens [margin annotation]

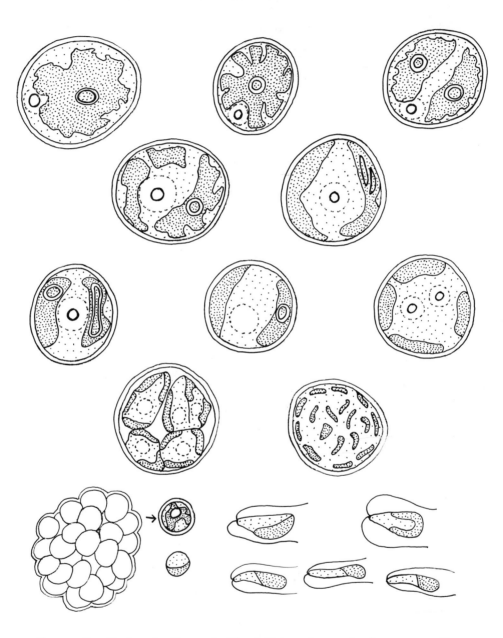

Figure 7.   *Trebouxia*, Group I: Vegetative and reproductive stages.   From "Some New and Interesting Species of *Trebouxia*, a Genus of Lichenized Algae," V. Ahmadjian, *American Journal of Botany*, 47 (1960), 680.

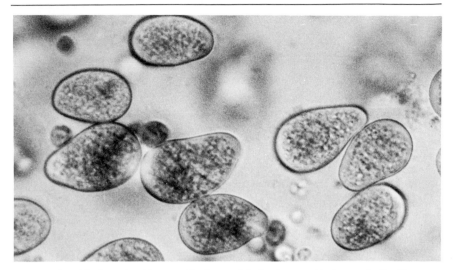

FIGURE 8. *Trebouxia* (Group I) from *Cladonia rangiferina*. Cells illustrate the egg-shaped form which is characteristic of Group I. (1000 x)

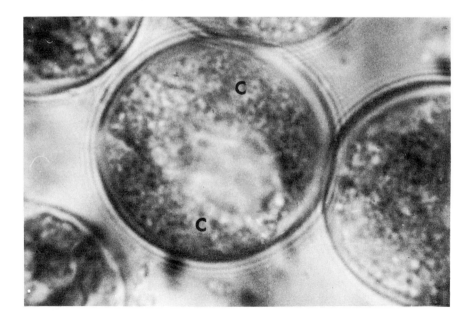

FIGURE 9. *Trebouxia* (Group I) from *Cladonia rangiferina*. Cell in the center of the photograph illustrates the parietal positions the chloroplast segments (c) assume after their first division. (3000 x)

(Figure 11) and each cell has a chloroplast that is not deeply incised. During division the halved chloroplast fragments remain in the center of the cell (Figure 12). *Trebouxia* belonging to the first group have been isolated from fruticose lichens, mainly *Cladonia* species, while those of the second group have been found in foliose and crustose forms. Sizes of

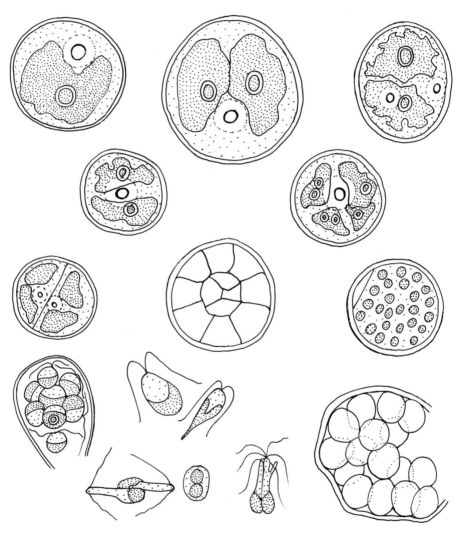

FIGURE 10. *Trebouxia*, Group II: Vegetative and reproductive stages. From "Some New and Interesting Species of *Trebouxia*," V. Ahmadjian, *American Journal of Botany*, 47 (1960), 682.

mature, vegetative cells in culture range from 11–34 microns.   In organic nutrient media the cells may contain many oil droplets and granules that obscure cellular details.   Under such conditions, the pyrenoids generally are indistinct.   Cells within a thallus, however, are free from oil droplets, and have distinct pyrenoids.   Some *Trebouxia* strains have gelatinous sheaths which are 5 microns wide (Figure 13).   A sheath is not seen around cells from a freshly fragmented thallus and apparently is a cultural characteristic.   The sheath has a watery consistency and can be revealed by adding India ink or a similar compound to a drop of liquid that contains the algal cells.

Trebouxia phycobionts cultured on organic nutrient agar form compact, elevated colonies that differ in color, shape, and size (Figure 14).   These characteristics are not constant and change according to the culture conditions [2, 3].

FIGURE 11.   *Trebouxia* (Group II) from *Xanthoria mawsoni*.   Cells illustrate the spherical form which is characteristic of Group II.   (2000 x)

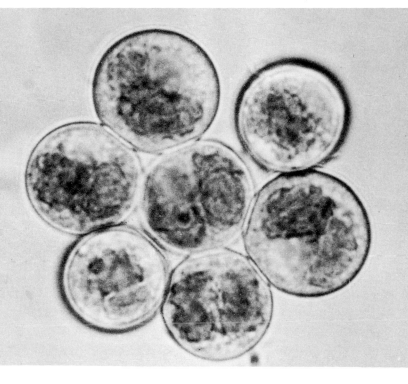

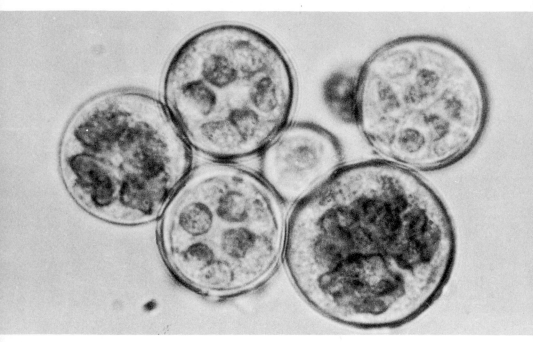

FIGURE 12.   *Trebouxia* (Group II) from *Candelaria concolor* v. *antarctica*. Cells illustrate the central positions the chloroplast segments assume during division.   (2000 x)

Reproductive Mechanisms

Blue-green phycobionts in the lichen multiply by vegetative cell division, by heterocysts and akinetes, both of which can germinate within the thallus [229], and by hormogonia.   Green phycobionts in the lichen multiply by vegetative cell division and/or by formation of asexual spores called aplanospores.   Aplanospores are miniatures of larger vegetative cells and are produced commonly by *Trebouxia* and related phycobionts, especially during spring (Figures 15, 16, 17).   Many more aplanospores, up to two hundred and fifty per sporangium, are produced under cultural conditions in organic nutrient medium than in a thallus, where the number of spores per sporangium ranges from two to thirty-two, more commonly two to eight.   The difference in spore number is due probably to the smaller amounts of nutrient materials that are available to algal cells within a thallus.   Each aplanospore increases to the size of a mature, vegetative cell and then divides to form more spores.   In liquid organic nutrient media,

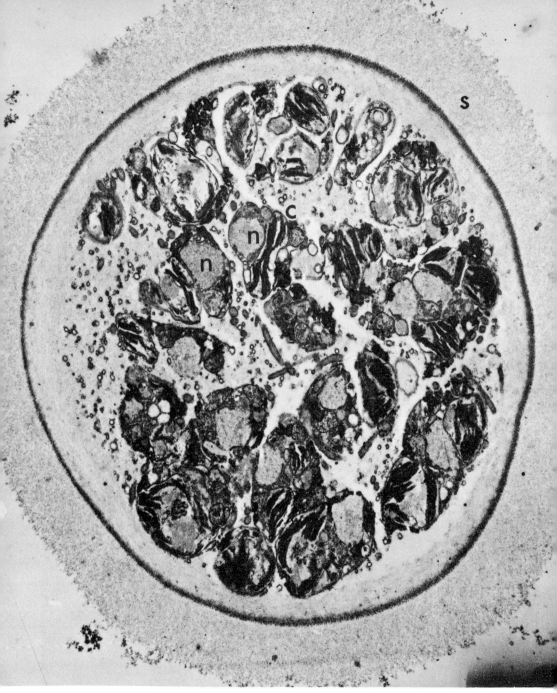

FIGURE 13. An electron micrograph of *Trebouxia* from *Parmelia caperata*. Cell contents have divided into many smaller units, each of which consists of a nucleus (n) and a portion of the chloroplast (c). A gelatinous sheath (s) surrounds the cell. (11,000 x)

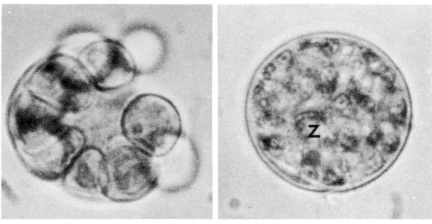

FIGURE 17   FIGURE 18

FIGURE 17. A ruptured aplanosporangium. Each aplanospore, after its release from the sporangium, enlarges to form a vegetative cell (*Trebouxia* from an unidentified lichen). (2000 x)

FIGURE 18. Sporangium with zoospores. Each crescent-shaped structure (z) represents the chloroplast of one zoospore (*Trebouxia* from *Candelaria concolor* v. *antarctica*). (2000 x)

by *Trebouxia* cells has not been observed in a thallus [3]. Cells within a thallus begin the initial stages of zoospore production, but during the final stages each protoplast segment forms a rigid cell wall and becomes an aplanospore. This is a result of the frequent periods of drying and wetting that lichens undergo in their natural habitats. These conditions favor the formation of aplanospores that resist drying better than the naked (= no cell wall) zoospores. Some *Trentepohliaceous* algae continue to form zoospores even while components of lichens [223].

FUNGAL SYMBIONT

Isolation Techniques

Many fungal components, or mycobionts [237], of lichens can be isolated and cultured. The best isolation method is by means of their spores. The fruiting bodies of lichens are of fungal origin so that the spores that are discharged from these fruits give rise only to fungi. The spore-isolation technique (Figure 19) involves little time and apparatus [7, 10, 135, 149, 241]. Freshly collected thalli give the best results, although some specimens have been used up to eight months after collection. After a month's storage at room temperature and in a dry condition the amount of spore discharge from a thallus decreases progressively [149].

First a thallus is soaked in cold water for about fifteen minutes. Individual fruiting bodies or small thallus fragments that contain several fruits of one lichen are blotted to remove excess water and fastened with a petroleum jelly to the upper half of a petri dish. Then the upper half of the dish is inverted over the lower half which contains a 2% agar layer or a soil-water agar medium (Appendix). The soil-water medium stimulates the germination of a greater variety of spores than a plain agar medium. In both media the amount of nutrients is so small that growth of contaminant organisms accidentally introduced on a plate is retarded, thereby allowing more time for spore germination of the mycobiont. As the fruiting bodies dry, spores are forceably discharged and fall onto the underlying agar surface. The spores are free of contaminants and emerge singly or in packets of four, eight, or, in some instances, one hundred or more. The discharged spores can reach heights of 0.1–3.0 cm and under natural conditions they are distributed easily by wind and air currents.

The greatest amount of spore discharge occurs during the slow drying of a wet fruiting body [16, 276, 297]. The drying causes a shrinkage and bursting of the spore sacs within the fruits (Figures 20, 21). A small amount of discharge also occurs when the fruits are wet. This is caused by an increase in turgor pressure and subsequent disruption of some spore sacs at their weak apical ends [139]. The percentage of spore discharge from lichens collected after a heavy rainfall is very small.

The rates of spore discharge and germination are variable [7]. *Cladonia* and *Baeomyces* species emit spores within minutes after their washed fruiting bodies are fixed to a petri dish, and after twelve to eighteen hours numerous clusters of their spores give a cloudy appearance to areas of the agar surface. Other lichens eject spores from two to twenty-four hours after drying begins. Germination time ranges from two hours in *Cladonia* species to twenty-four hours in other lichens and up to five weeks for *Ramalina ecklonii* [94]. Spores from crustose lichens such as *Acarospora*, *Lecidea*, and *Lecanora* (Figure 22) germinate faster than those of foliose forms like *Cetraria*, *Parmelia*, and *Xanthoria* (Figure 23). Spore activity would have to be of considerable importance to crustose lichens since they

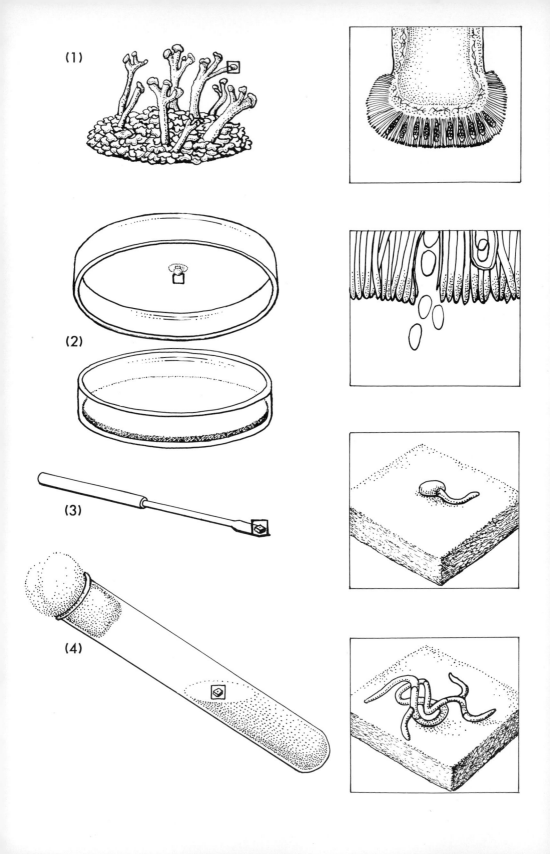

(1)

(2)

(3)

(4)

generally lack means of vegetative reproduction. Also, crustose lichens adhere so tightly to their substratum that chances of fragmentation are less than in the loosely-attached foliose forms.

Spores on the agar surface can be observed microscopically without opening the petri dish by placing the inverted dish on a microscope stage and examining under low magnification (100x). Numerous droplets of sap from the spore sacs sometimes can be seen near the discharged spores. After spore germination has occurred, the petri dish is placed under a dissecting microscope and its cover is removed. With proper magnification the spores will be visible. By means of a sterilized spear needle or other suitable instrument, a block of agar with one or many spores is cut out and transferred to a test tube that contains an organic nutrient medium such as a malt-yeast extract agar (Appendix). There are several variations to this technique. The plate may be flooded with sterile, distilled water and the spores then isolated with a micropipette, or a fruiting body can be positioned so that its spores are discharged into a drop of sterile water and single spores then isolated with a micropipette. Or the plates may be inverted with the agar surface directly above the fruiting bodies so that the spores are discharged up onto the agar. Foreign organisms on the isolation plates can be recognized easily and avoided.

From a random collection of lichens the discharged spores of about half the species will germinate. The reasons that spores of many lichens fail to germinate are not understood. A few experiments designed to break spore dormancy by alterations of the pH, temperature, and culture medium have had limited success [94, 241]. Bark extract and compounds such as erythritol, pectin, and glycerol speeded the germination rates of spores of *Xanthoria parietina* [21]. Spores covered with contaminant bacteria germinated faster and had a more vigorous initial growth rate than those uncontaminated [146, 277]. A similar stimulatory effect was caused by

FIGURE 19. (opposite) A lichen fungus is cultured by allowing its spores to germinate. A lichen (1) is soaked in water and a fruiting body (right) is removed and affixed to the top of a petri dish (2). The spore sacs (asci) rupture (right), discharging spores onto the agar layer in the bottom of the dish. After some spores have germinated, a block of agar with spores on it is excised (3). Transferred to a culture tube (4), the spores grow into a mass of fungal hyphae (right). From "The Fungi of Lichens," V. Ahmadjian. Copyright © 1963 by *Scientific American, Inc.* All rights reserved.

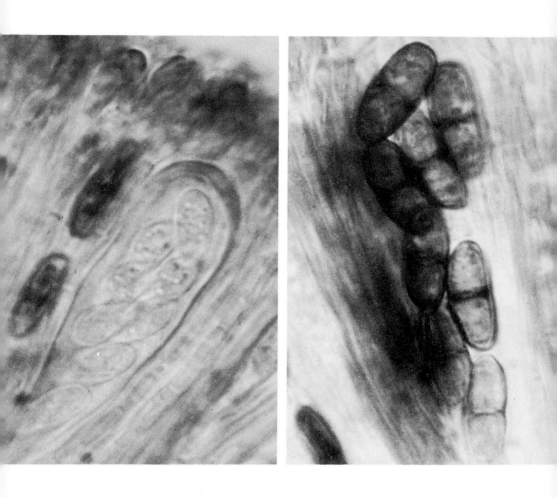

FIGURE 20. An ascus of *Physcia stellaris* which contains eight immature asco-spores. (2000 x)

FIGURE 21. An ascus of *Physcia stellaris* which contains eight mature asco-spores. (2000 x)

thiamine [277]. *Peltigera* spores have germinated only in an extract of the lichen phycobiont [241]. The percentage of spore discharge and germination among many temperate-zone lichens is highest in early spring and fall, when the most favorable climatic conditions for these processes generally occur [149]. In some lichens spore discharge and germination occur throughout the year [238]. The percentage of germination ranges

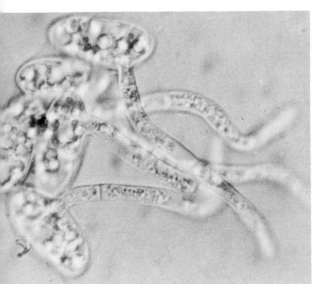 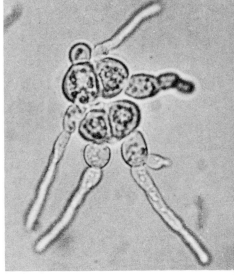

FIGURE 22   FIGURE 23

FIGURE 22. Germinated ascospores of *Lecanora* sp., a few days after the spores were discharged onto an agar surface. (2000 x) From Ahmadjian, 1963 [10].

FIGURE 23. Germinated ascospores of *Xanthoria parietina*, a few days after the spores were discharged onto an agar surface. (2000 x)

from 90% or more in many species to forms in which only a few germinate out of hundreds of spores. Some lichens, notably species of *Collema*, have a high percentage of spore germination, but further growth of the germ tubes does not occur even after transfer to an organic nutrient medium, except perhaps during certain periods of the year. The only successful cultivation of a *Collema* mycobiont was derived from a specimen collected in February when snow still covered the ground [126, 130].

Mycobionts of lichens without fruiting bodies or whose spores fail to germinate sometimes can be isolated by means of the hyphae that make up the thallus. With foliose forms removal of the upper cortex and algal layer will reveal a medullary layer that is solely fungal in nature. Small strands of this tissue can be teased out and inoculated into a culture medium. Large fragments of fungal hyphae which surround algal cells in a thallus can also give rise to colonies when they are isolated by means of a micropipette and inoculated onto a nutrient agar. In both instances contamination is a serious problem, and once a colony has formed there is no assurance that it is the real fungal component and not a contaminant organism growing on or within the thallus.

Classification and Description

Representatives of three major classes of fungi form lichen or lichenlike associations. Most of the true lichen associations are formed by members of the *Ascomycetes*. The *Deuteromycetes* or Imperfect Fungi are represented by a dozen or more genera. The *Basidiomycetes* form several lichenlike associations in tropical regions [176] and a few associations in temperate areas which appear to be true lichens [202].

Cultural Characteristics

Most isolated lichen fungi do not resemble the *composite plant*. A few have a form suggestive of that of a lichen thallus but the structural organization is absent [7]. On agar media cultured mycobionts form compact, elevated colonies (Figure 24) [10] whose consistencies are generally so hard that in some forms cutting small portions for transfer may be a difficult task. Many tropical mycobionts and a few temperate region forms, especially species of *Graphis* and related genera, have thick gelatinous sheaths around their hyphae [11]. Sheaths of this type with their capabilities for water absorption and retention must play important roles in the water relations of the lichens which these mycobionts form. Mycobiont colonies differ in size, shape, and color. There appears to be almost as much diversity among cultured fungal components as there is among the lichens from which they are isolated. Even among single-spore isolates from one fruiting body there was variety among the colonies [11]. However, in some instances the isolated mycobionts of different lichens (for example, from species of *Cladonia*) may be identical with regard to morphology, size, and pigmentation of colonies.

FIGURE 24. Colony of the cultured mycobiont *Cladonia cristatella*. The colony, grown for six months on an agar medium, measures about 4 cm in diameter and 1.5 cm in height. (4 x) From Ahmadjian, 1963 [10].

Reproductive Mechanisms

One unfortunate aspect in any effort to establish a relationship between fungi which form lichens and free-living molds is that most isolated and cultured lichen fungi are sterile—that is, they do not produce spores. One hypothesis states that lichen fungi are free-living, imperfect molds which form perfect or fruiting stages only after they have entered into a lichenized state [111]. This is not an illogical possibility, since lichen fungi must have originated from free-living forms, but there is little evidence to support this view.

Several hundred mycobionts have been cultured and a few have produced asexual spores or conidia (Figure 25) [10, 11]. Of the structures described as conidia [280, 295] some are nothing more than the swollen cells of vegetative hyphae, a common characteristic of lichen fungi [11] and in general fungi [165] under varying cultural conditions. Hale [111] isolated a fungus, from the lichen *Buellia stillingiana* and found it to be identical, in terms of the conidia which it produced, to the free-living, imperfect mold *Sporidesmium folliculatum*, a common saprophyte on wood in northeastern North America. Attempts to duplicate his results have not been successful [12]. The mycobiont *Phaeographina fulgurata* forms abundant conidia [10, 11], but attempts to relate this fungus to free-living molds have been unsuccessful. Another conidial-producing mycobiont is *Lecidea erratica*, which in its lichenized state occurs commonly on exposed rocks in northeastern United States. A dozen isolates of this mycobiont from specimens of different localities have verified the regularity of spore production. Its conidia are small, colorless, single celled, and are budded off from

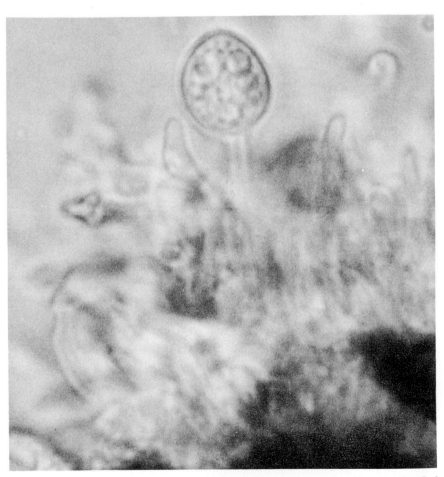

FIGURE 25. An asexual spore or conidium produced at the tip of a hyphal branch by the mycobiont *Phaeographina fulgurata* in culture. (3500 x) From Ahmadjian, 1963 [10].

the hyphae [10]. They accumulate in gelatinous masses which are distributed over the colony surface. The manner by which the spores are formed is identical to that of the imperfect, free-living fungus *Aureobasidium* (= *Pullularia*) *pullulans*, an organism which is extremely common, highly polymorphic, and has adapted to a wide variety of habitats [62]. This fungus and related strains form symbiotic relationships with algae and insects, and it is conceivable that some strains of this fungus, possibly mutant forms, were capable of forming lichenized associations. Further isolations of mycobionts from the fifteen to twenty thousand species of lichens undoubtedly will reveal additional relationships between lichen fungi and free-living fungi. Some *Buellia* and *Cladonia* mycobionts produce abundant pycnidia and pycniospores in culture but the spores do not germinate [11, 14].

Physiology of
3 ✖ Lichen Symbionts

The physiology of lichens can be studied with the isolated symbionts in axenic culture or with the *composite plants*. The method which is chosen depends on the information an investigator wishes to obtain. By studying the isolated partners one may make critical analyses of nutritional requirements and the influence of micronutrients such as vitamins on growth. Cultures can be maintained for long periods of time since they will not contain contaminant organisms. The information obtained from such investigations can be extended with caution to naturally occurring associations. One must remember that under natural conditions the *composite plants* are exposed to many variables, such as temperature, light, moisture, type and pH of substratum, and nature and number of epiphytic organisms —these conditions differ from those of laboratory cultures. Studies of lichen thalli can elucidate problems of ecological behavior, like the manner and rate of water absorption and resistance to environmental extremes as well as physiological activities such as respiration, photosynthesis, and nutrient translocation. It would be helpful if lichen thalli could be grown in axenic cultures, but all attempts to do this have encountered several obstacles. First, it is difficult to rid a thallus or even part of it of foreign organisms like bacteria, free-living fungi, and algae. Second, a lichen association is very labile. The partnership exists only as long as growth conditions are unfavorable for both components. A change in environment, such as a period of prolonged moisture, causes an unbalanced growth between the partners and thus a breakdown of the union. It is difficult to even maintain a lichen in a laboratory culture, because any addition of nutrients to the culture medium or excessive light and moisture will cause an unbalanced growth. The only way to support a lichen in a laboratory for any length of time is to provide it with the same conditions which it encounters in nature, the most important of which are a low nutrient supply and alternate drying and wetting. This, however, can become discouraging because the average annual growth rate of these associations is only a few millimeters in diameter. One solution to this problem would be to reestablish the association in laboratory culture beginning with the isolated symbionts. This has been accomplished to some extent [8, 10, 13]. However, a resynthesis solves the problem of obtaining axenic cultures of the *composite plants* but not that of their slow growth.

ৰু

ALGAL SYMBIONT

Cultural Methods

The cultural requirements of lichen algae are similar to those of free-living algae. Blue-green and green phycobionts can be cultured on illuminated liquid or agar media which contain mineral salts (Appendix). With green phycobionts, especially *Trebouxia*, growth is stimulated greatly if a carbon source is added to the medium. In a sugar medium light is not essential because the sugar can be absorbed from the medium. Thus, growth and development of these algae can take place in total darkness. Generally, growth is slower and colony color paler when a culture is kept in darkness [9]. Facultative heterotrophy—that is, the ability of an organism to grow in either light or dark conditions—is common among green phycobionts with one exception. *Coccobotrys verrucariae*, a phycobiont of *Verrucaria nigrescens*, is unable to grow in darkness on a medium supplied with glucose [61]. Several blue-green phycobionts, species of *Nostoc*, have been isolated into bacteria-free cultures [124, 292], but it is not known whether or not they can grow heterotrophically.

Nutrition

NITROGEN REQUIREMENTS • It is impossible to generalize on the utilization of nitrogenous compounds by lichen algae since most of the investigations in this respect have been conducted with different strains of *Trebouxia* [2, 61, 140, 174, 208, 214, 271, 291]. However, in this genus with few exceptions growth is more pronounced—strikingly so in many cases—when a source of organic nitrogen is in the culture medium. This stimulatory effect occurs only if a carbon source is included in the medium. An organic nitrogen source substituted for an inorganic one in a mineral medium does not enhance growth except, as with peptone, if the compound can be used as a source of carbon. The best organic nitrogen source varies according to the particular algal strain, but those most favored are asparagine, glycine, peptone, and alanine. Acetamine, leucine, and urea are good sources for some strains and poor for others. Sources of inorganic nitrogen which support optimal growth are the ammonium salts followed by nitrates. Growth of some *Trebouxia* is as strong with ammonium salts for nitrogen sources as with amino acids. Nitrites do not support growth of *Trebouxia*, although they can be used by other phycobionts such as strains of *Stichococcus* [214]. Some *Trebouxia* phycobionts liquify gelatine, a compound which contains a high proportion of glycine. *Trebouxia* phycobionts from *Cladonia* species are micronitrophilous [140] —that is, they can develop in a glucose-mineral salts medium without added nitrogen. Under similar conditions phycobionts of other lichens either fail to grow or develop very slowly and their cells become yellowish and filled with fatty materials.

With respect to the nitrogen requirements of other genera of phycobionts —namely, *Coccomyxa, Chlorella, Hyalococcus,* and *Stichococcus*—there is no clear, discernible preference for organic rather than inorganic sources of nitrogen.

Fixation of atmospheric nitrogen has not been shown to occur in a green algal symbiont [236] but has been demonstrated for *Nostoc* phycobionts both in their lichenized [45, 236] and nonlichenized [124, 292] states. Some of this fixed nitrogen is excreted by the alga [124, 125] and under natural conditions is transferred to the mycobiont [236]. The possible significance of this in the lichen symbiosis is obvious.

CARBON REQUIREMENTS • *Trebouxia* have been the most commonly used test organisms for carbon nutrition studies. Glucose and fructose are the best carbon sources, followed by galactose, sucrose, maltose, and mannitol.

Salts of organic acids support some growth but in general are poor carbon sources [61, 208].

In most cases light increases growth in a sugar medium, especially one with a high concentration of sugar [140]. It is not known whether the strong growth in light is due to an increased rate of sugar uptake from the medium or the added effect of CO_2 assimilation. The latter process has been shown to be inhibited by the presence of glucose in a growth medium [61]. Manco [174] used $C^{14}O_2$ and found that *Trebouxia* fixed three to six times more carbon in the absence of glucose in light.

Trebouxia phycobionts grow well in media that contain high concentrations of minerals and sugars. They can tolerate concentrations (up to 20% glucose) which are inhibitory to many free-living algae [94, 140] (Figure 26).

VITAMINS, GROWTH SUBSTANCES, AND INHIBITORS • Lichen algae do not need exogenous sources of vitamins [208, 302]. On the contrary, there is evidence that these algae excrete vitamins [39, 128, 302]. Growth of tested strains of *Trebouxia* and *Coccomyxa* was not influenced by thiamine

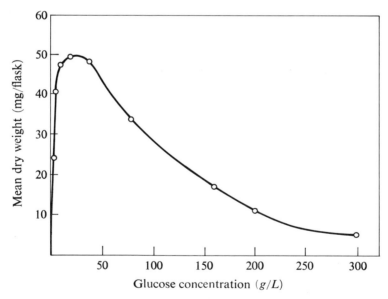

FIGURE 26. Growth of *Trebouxia erici* (from *Cladonia cristatella*) in Bold's solution with different concentrations of glucose (nitrate as N source). Incubation was for 21 days at 20C, and under continuous illumination (90 ft.c.). From Fox, 1965 [95].

(0.1–1 mg/liter) or biotin (5 μg/liter) or various combinations of vitamins (Vitamins B_1, B_2, B_6, C, nicotinamide, pantothenic acid, m-inositol, and biotin or Vitamins D_2, E, tocopherolacetate, 2-methyl-naphtoquinone, and β-carotene; each compound except biotin and Vitamin D_2, which were of lower concentrations, had a final concentration of 10 mg/liter). The vitamins were added to a sugar-minerals medium as well as a minerals medium. Ascorbic acid (Vitamin C) (1 mg/liter) in a hydrogen atmosphere with 5% CO_2, stimulated the growth of *Trebouxia* on an inorganic, mineral medium. Under these conditions growth was comparable to that which occurred on a sugar medium. A closely related compound, dioxymaleic acid, had a similar stimulatory effect [208]. Because of the ease by which ascorbic acid is oxidized and reduced, it can play an important role in photosynthesis, specifically in photosynthetic phosphorylation, thus accounting for its action in growth stimulation. An interesting hypothesis which has been proposed [208] is that ascorbic acid or related compounds, perhaps even lichen acids, play a role in the lichen symbiosis by stimulating the photosynthetic rates of lichen algae. Ascorbic acid has not been found in isolated mycobionts, but its presence has been reported in several arctic lichens [109].

Extracts of free-living fungi and yeast (10 g/liter) speeded the initial heterotrophic growth of some *Trebouxia* [208], although with other strains yeast extract (5 g/liter) was inhibitory [9]. Indoleacetic acid (IAA) (50–100 mg/liter) was stimulatory to two species of *Trebouxia* [77], one a phycobiont of *Xanthoria parietina* and the other a free-living form; but at lower concentrations (1.25–10 mg/liter) IAA inhibited the growth of other *Trebouxia* strains [162, 302]. Gibberellic acid (5–15 mg/liter) did not stimulate growth of *Trebouxia* (77). Streptomycin, which bleaches chlorophyll and prevents chlorophyll synthesis by algae, was lethal to *Trebouxia* and *Coccomyxa* at concentrations of 10–25 mg/liter but penicillin (0.2–5 mg/liter) had no effect on their growth [303]. A *Nostoc* phycobiont of *Collema tenax* under cultural conditions excreted unknown substances which inhibited the growth of its fungal partner [127].

Growth Rate

Lichen algae, with generation times of days and sometimes weeks [12], are slow growers when compared to other algae.

Several methods can be used to measure growth rates of lichen algae.

With liquid cultures the number of cells in a given volume of suspension can be counted at periodic intervals during the growth period [208]. This can be accomplished by a hemocytometer or other comparable device. A disadvantage to this technique, aside from its tediousness, is that *Trebouxia* cells tend to remain together in clumps which are difficult to dissociate. One way to reduce clumping is to place the algal suspension in a blender for a few seconds. Another method is to pass the suspension through a sterile glass wool [174]. Clumping is caused by a failure of the aplanospores to separate. Another problem is whether one counts as a single unit a sporangium that contains several hundred aplanospores, which may or may not separate, or which may do so only partially. Moreover, these algae have a wide range of sizes, which make it difficult to select cells for average size determinations. Growth rates can be measured by centrifugation of the culture and determination of cell volume [291], by dry weight, and optical density. The latter method is accomplished by a colorimeter or a turbidimeter which give rapid and fairly accurate measurements. One point of caution is that the intensity of green color of many phycobionts varies among different strains and also in a single strain grown on different organic additives and exposed to different light and temperature conditions.

The most frequent method of determining the growth of algae on solid substrates has been colony size. *Trebouxia* form distinctive colonies on organic agar medium [3]. The volume of these colonies can be determined and growth curves calculated by measuring colonies of different ages. By measuring the height and diameter of a colony one can determine the volume of one-half of a prolate spheroid or of a spherical segment, depending on whether the height is greater or less than, respectively, one-half the diameter [2, 6]. The colony size method for determining growth is not particularly accurate since different algal strains produce colonies of varying density.

Fox [95], from his studies of the photosynthetic growth of *Trebouxia*, determined a growth constant of 0.09 for *T. erici*. This is much less than what has been reported for other photosynthetic microorganisms [137]. The slow growth rates of lichen algae do not appear to be related to any deficiency in their ability to take up CO_2. Fox found that *Trebouxia* took up $C^{14}O_2$ as rapidly as *Chlorella*. The distribution of its fixed carbon into "permanent" (= ethanol insoluble) cell structures, however, occurred much slower. Excretion of fixed carbon into the culture medium was also less than that by *Chlorella*. Smith and Drew [258] reported similar results with a *Nostoc* phycobiont: that is, once carbon had been fixed photosynthetically it remained in an ethanol soluble form for a relatively long time and the formation of insoluble reserve compounds proceeded very slowly. The authors concluded that, "In the lichen, the growth of the algal cells is severely restricted, but the ability to photosynthesize much less so. Since most of the carbon fixed in photosynthesis cannot be directed to growth processes (as it would be in a free-living alga), as soon as the limited capacity of the algal cells to store fixed carbon is saturated, it is inevitable that carbon compounds should move out of the algal cells to the surrounding thallus tissue. This is, therefore, one more reason for supposing that the slow growth of lichens is a significant aspect of their physiology." The fact that *Nostoc* can excrete large quantities of organic compounds may explain why this alga, in the lichenized state, unlike *Trebouxia*, is usually not penetrated by fungal haustoria.

Factors Influencing Growth

TEMPERATURE • There is considerable information on the optimal growth temperatures of lichen algae. Variation exists and depends on the strain of algae and on the medium on which they are grown. Cells of *Trebouxia* isolated from different parts of a thallus as well as those isolated from one lichen species collected at different localities may show different temperature optima [271]. Optimal growth temperatures may vary by 3C according to whether the nitrogen source of a medium is asparagine or peptone [2]. Some generalizations can be made. *Trebouxia* from *Cladonia* grow best between 18–23C, those from *Caloplaca, Candelariella, Physcia,* and *Xanthoria* between 12–15C, and from *Lecanora, Parmelia,* and *Stereocaulon* between 12–24C [271]. *Trebouxia* phycobionts from Antarctic lichens have an optimal temperature range of 10–15C [12]. The temperature range at which *Trebouxia* will show some growth is 1–27C. For most strains 18–20C is best. Temperature optima of other genera of phycobionts such as *Chlorella, Coccomyxa, Hyalococcus, Myrmecia, Stichococcus,* and *Trentepohlia* do not differ from the limits and optima described for *Trebouxia* strains [2, 214, 271]. A *Nostoc* phycobiont of *Collema tenax* grew optimally at 25C [129].

pH • The optimal pH range for *Trebouxia* is 4.0–7.4 [140, 208]. For a *Nostoc* phycobiont it is 6.0–9.9 [129].

LIGHT • Early investigators of lichen algae who kept their cultures under light from a northerly exposed window discovered that colonies of some strains lost their green color after a certain period of time [140, 291].

Decoloration occurred slowly in diffuse daylight but very rapidly, within one or two days, under direct summer sunlight. The elevated temperature caused by the light was one explanation proposed for this loss of color, and another was the reduction of nitrogen in the medium. Neither explanation was satisfactory in some cases because decoloration occurred under conditions where optimal growth temperatures were constant and nitrogen supplies adequate. Decoloration occurred with algae grown on mineral as well as sugar media and in liquid or solid media. In many instances the colorless cells were not dead and could be restored to normal color and growth when transferred to a sugar-nitrogen medium and kept in darkness. When strains of *Trebouxia decolorans*, phycobiont of *Buellia punctata* and *Xanthoria parietina*, were grown under artificial light and in mineral media, growth stopped and decoloration began at light intensities above 100 ft.c. [2, 3]. The reason for this color loss is not known but one clue may lie in the type of pigmentation of these light-sensitive algae. When pigments were extracted from strains of *T. decolorans* and compared with those of a nonsensitive, nonlichenized *Trebouxia*, it was found that both algae had the same type of pigments—namely, chlorophylls a, b, beta-carotene, lutein, and violaxanthin. The difference was in the amount of pigments. The phycobionts contained more chlorophyll and carotenoids but less beta-carotene than the free-living form. Moreover, the chlorophyll/carotenoid ratio was higher in the free-living, nonlichenized alga [74]. One of the roles attributed to carotenoids of green algae is that they protect chlorophyll from the destructive effects of light. Although *T. decolorans* has a higher xanthophyll content than its free-living counterpart, the amount of carotene is much less. Both lichens which contain this phycobiont have a pigmented cortex that reduces the amount of light which passes through it to the algal layer. Bruchet [50] did not find significant differences between the pigments of lichen algae (*Trebouxia, Coccomyxa, Hyalococcus*) and free-living algae.

The light-intensity range for optimal growth of *Trebouxia* is 150–250 ft.c. [12].

Lichen Substances

The role which algal symbionts have in the synthesis of lichen substances has not been investigated fully. Extracts and examination of pure cultures of *Trebouxia* have not revealed identifiable substances [208]. Algal symbionts may play key roles in the biosynthesis of lichen compounds because most lichen fungi do not produce in culture the same compounds which they do while in a lichenized state. None of the hundreds of isolated mycobionts have produced a depside or depsidone—diphenyl structures which are the commonest types of lichen compounds—but they have produced the monocyclic compounds such as orsellinic and haematommic acids which make up these structures [133]. These compounds are not found in the corresponding *composite plants* possibly because under the natural conditions of the symbiosis they are converted rapidly into the diphenyl structures. Depside hydrolyzing enzymes have been found in lichens [290] and the isolated phycobiont [190]. Hess [133] suggested that the algae may promote coupling of the monocyclic structures produced by the mycobionts and also produce the specific modifications which characterize different lichen compounds.

Physiological Strains

Physiological strains of lichen algae, mostly *Trebouxia*, are common [2, 3, 271]. Strains of *Trebouxia* derived from single cells isolated from one thallus have shown differences in nutrition, growth rate, and temperature optimum, although the cells of each strain were morphologically identical. This finding is surprising because sexuality of these algae supposedly does not occur within a thallus. If the algae in a thallus reproduce only by asexual means, they should be of a fairly homogeneous nature. The heterogeneity which exists suggests three possibilities. First, these organisms have a high mutation rate. Second, the sexual process does take place within a thallus. Third, a lichen incorporates other algal types during its growth period. The latter possibility seems the most likely. An important method of lichen dispersal is by small thallus structures called isidia and soredia. These asexual reproductive structures, particularly soredia are produced in large quantities by many lichens and are distributed to different habitats by wind and rain [49, 107]. The fungal margins of actively growing lichens undoubtedly encounter and incorporate some of these fragments, the algae of which may survive and proliferate within foreign thalli. Some algae which are incorporated may be free-living types, a few of which may also survive [5]. The fact that different strains of algae exist within a single thallus or in thalli of a particular species causes a problem when one tries to compare isolated phycobionts. It may also explain why early investigators who isolated algae from the same lichen species obtained different results.

Extracellular Products and Permeability

Lichen algae excrete organic substances into their growth media. A *Nostoc* symbiont of *Collema tenax* excreted about 5% of the nitrogen it fixed from the atmosphere, as well as polysaccharides and the following vitamins: thiamine, biotin, riboflavin, nicotinic acid, and pantothenic acid [128]. A *Coccomyxa* phycobiont of *Peltigera aphthosa* excreted biotin and thiamine, the former in amounts 14–16 times greater than a free-living species of *Chlorella* [38, 39]. Other strains of *Trebouxia* and *Coccomyxa* phycobionts excreted thiamine [302]. The excretion of various compounds has been reported for free-living blue-green and green algae as well [89]. It is interesting to correlate this information to the relationship that exists between the *Nostoc* phycobiont and its fungal symbiont. Unlike most lichens, the association between the partners of *Collema* is a loose one [73]. There are no penetrations of the algal cells by fungal hyphae. Rather, the hyphae grow between the algal filaments, and some may pass into their gelatinous sheaths. It can be postulated that because the alga excretes substances on which the fungus can grow [126], even though slowly, the more intimate contacts do not develop. It is not known to what extent green phycobionts excrete organic materials other than vitamins, but free-living green algae excrete soluble polysaccharides [89]. The excretion of vitamins, especially biotin and thiamine, by lichen algae fits in well with the fact that many lichen fungi require biotin and thiamine for growth [7, 11, 112]. The fact that some green lichen algae liquify gelatine suggests that they excrete a proteolytic enzyme.

In a study of the membrane permeability of phycobiont cells Follmann [90] compared the rate of permeability of *Trebouxia* cells from a freshly-fragmented lichen (*Cladonia furcata*) with cells of a month-old axenic culture of the same phycobiont and a free-living alga, *Chlorococcum humicolum*, which was isolated from the same substrate as the lichen. The cells were first plasmolyzed in a 0.6 mol/liter solution of glucose and then, as glucose molecules entered the cells and water was reabsorbed, the rate of deplasmolysis or expansion of the protoplast for each group was determined. By measuring the amount of time (up to forty-eight hours) it took for the protoplasts to regain their initial volume, it was possible to measure the relative rate of entry of glucose molecules into the cells. The rate of permeability to glucose was greatest in algal cells from the freshly fragmented thallus, followed by cells from the month-old axenic culture and then the free-living alga. Follmann speculated that lichen compounds, which are produced by the fungal partners, increase permeability of the algal cells within a thallus and thereby facilitate movement of food molecules from alga to fungus. It has been shown with animals and plants that lichen substances increase cell permeability [92a, 284].

Resistance to Environmental Extremes

Lichen algae can withstand temperature extremes provided they are in a dried state. The resistance of these algae within thalli is 40–50C less when they are moist than when dry—i.e., 43–46C as compared to 80–100C [154]. Their resistance to heat also decreases after they have been cultured for several weeks. Lange [154] found that cells of a *Trebouxia* phycobiont of *Cladonia foliacea* v. *convoluta* were damaged after a one-half hour exposure to 90C while cells of the same alga after nine weeks of culture became injured after 70C over the same period of exposure. He found also that variability in heat resistance existed among algae of lichens from different habitats. Phycobionts of lichens whose natural habitats were shady were strongly damaged at 70C, while those from sun-exposed lichens withstood temperatures up to 100C. Lichen algae still can grow at 0C [214], and CO_2 absorption of the *composite plants*, which would be caused largely by the algal partner, was shown to occur even at lower temperatures [144, 156, 157].

Lichen algae differ in their abilities to withstand dry periods. As expected, the differences in tolerance are reflected in the ecological habitats of the *composite plants*. Ried [217] found that a dry period of six to twelve days at 40–60% humidity caused a strong and irreversible inhibition of photosynthesis of *Verrucaria elaeomelaena* (phycobiont = *Heterococcus caespitosus*) a permanently submerged, aquatic lichen. With periodically submerged lichens, such as *Dermatocarpon fluviatile* (phycobiont = *Hyalococcus dermatocarponis*), there was a strong initial photosynthetic inhibition which, however, became almost wholly reversible within a few days. Land lichens were even more resistant. *Rhizocarpon geographicum* (phycobiont = *Trebouxia* sp.) was extremely drought-resistant, and its photosynthetic process was affected only slightly after six months' drying. The effect which drying has on lichen algae depends not only on the length of a dry period but also on the degree and speed of drying. For example, with *D. fluviatile* there was a stronger initial photosynthetic inhibition after twelve hours' drying over concentrated H_2SO_4 than after a five-day drying at 40% humidity, or even a twenty-seven day drying at 60% humidity.

With R. *geographicum*, however, even drying over concentrated H_2SO_4 had little effect on photosynthesis. Inhibition of photosynthesis caused by drying is not directly proportional to the length of a dry period. A dry period of a few days may have the same effect on photosynthesis as longer periods, and significant injury results only after extremely dry periods of weeks or months. Thus, a series of short-term, dry periods, each of which strongly decreases photosynthesis for a few days and thereby depletes the food reserves, may be of more harm than one prolonged dry period [217].

Trebouxia from species of *Alectoria* remained viable after five weeks in an air-dried condition, while those of *Cladonia* survived as long as six to eight months [154]. Culturing the algae for any length of time prior to the experiments reduced their tolerance. For example, cells of a *Coccomyxa* phycobiont from a freshly collected thallus of *Solorina saccata* were injured after twenty-three weeks in a dried state, but the same alga cultured for nine weeks in a liquid medium became damaged after only five weeks' drying. There is a report [213] of the survival of a *Trebouxia* after three years in a dry thallus of *Xanthoria parietina*. Some soil algae like *Nostoc* and *Chlorococcum* are more resistant to dessication than *Trebouxia* [248]. These algae—and probably the same is true for *Trebouxia*—have highly viscous protoplasts with small vacuoles and very low water contents. Moisture is imbibed within the gel-like protoplasts and is bound firmly, even under air-dried conditions [99]. One reason why *Trebouxia* is found so commonly in lichen associations is due undoubtedly to its drought-resistant qualities.

Lichens often are described as being one of the hardiest groups of plants. Whenever there is speculation on the type of life that may be found or could survive under the extreme environmental conditions of other planets like Mars, lichens are mentioned. Whether or not they could survive under the known conditions of some extraterrestrial environments, without consideration of how they might have originated on other planets, is still a matter of speculation. One study [33] has provided some information in this respect. The phycobiont *Trebouxia erici*, isolated from *Cladonia cristatella*, was subjected to a simulated Martian environment with the following characteristics: atmosphere composed of 95.7% nitrogen, 4.0% argon, 0.3% carbon dioxide, and less than 1% oxygen; pressure at 85 mm of mercury; temperature range from 26–30C during the day (15½ hrs.) to —60C at night (8½ hrs.); light greater than 4800 Å at an intensity range of 300–500 ft.c.; moisture less than 0.5% of soil weight or less than 0.01

ml/cm² of soil; soil consisted of 50% 10-mesh felsite and 50% pulverized limonite. Under these conditions *T. erici* survived for about two weeks.

ફ⋗

FUNGAL SYMBIONT

Cultural Methods

Lichen fungi are not difficult organisms to culture provided one has the patience to endure their slow growth. A variety of media have been used for this purpose. Malt-yeast extract agar (Appendix) supports the strongest growth of many mycobionts [16, 94, 129]. Early investigators attempted to increase the growth rates of these organisms by an assortment of complex media [271] including currant, carrot, plum, and beef extracts, but with little success. The problem of the slow growth of these forms probably will not be resolved by manipulation of their culture media but rather through genetic changes such as mutations.

Stock cultures of lichen fungi can be maintained for five years or longer in screw-cap test tubes or bottles which are kept at 5–8C.

Nutrition

NITROGEN REQUIREMENTS • Many nitrogenous compounds can be used by lichen fungi. The degree of utilization of a particular compound depends on the fungal strain and the culture medium. For example, the type of carbon source in a medium can influence the kinds of nitrogen compounds which can be used. An *Xanthoria parietina* mycobiont grown in a liquid medium used a greater variety of nitrogen compounds, both organic and inorganic, when the carbon source was pectin rather than sucrose [21]. Lichen fungi readily use ammonium salts, nitrates, gelatine (which many forms can liquify [296]) peptone, urea, and casein hydrolysate [11]. There is no marked preference for organic rather than inorganic sources of nitrogen. Amino acids which support strong growth include L-proline, L-alanine, L-arginine, L-glutamic acid, L-aspartic acid, and L-asparagine [108, 279] (Figure 27). Lichen fungi have not been shown to fix atmospheric nitrogen [208]

CARBON REQUIREMENTS • The disaccharides cellobiose, maltose, lactose, and sucrose are best for many lichen fungi. Hexose sugars such as glucose, galactose, fructose, mannose, rhamnose, and sorbose also are utilized well. Some polysaccharides such as dextrin, dextran, and pectin are good sources, while others like cellulose and soluble starch are used to a limited extent. Other sugars, alcohols, and Krebs Cycle acids are used to varying degrees [11, 21, 114, 129, 179].

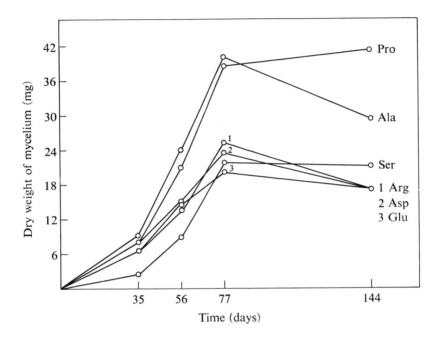

FIGURE 27.   Growth curves of the mycobiont *Acarospora fuscata* in a basal medium (glucose, minerals, biotin, thiamine) containing amino acids (as N sources) which supported the best growth.   Pro, proline; Ala, alanine; Ser, serine; Arg, arginine; Asp, aspartic acid; Glu, glutamic acid.   From Gross and Ahmadjian, 1966 [108].

The shape and size of a mycobiont's cells, its production of extracellular metabolites such as pigments and crystals, and its formation of gelatinous sheaths vary considerably according to the type of carbon source in the growth medium [11, 21].   When a *Graphina bipartita* mycobiont was cultured with lactose as a carbon source, it excreted a bright yellow pigment into the medium, had many red crystals encrusted on its hyphae and had a pronounced gelatinous sheath.   With maltose the pigment produced was a darker yellow, crystals were present, the sheath was not pronounced,

and the hyphae had many swollen cells. With sucrose there was a prominent sheath, pigments and crystals were not formed, the hyphae were con-
torted, and the cells were small, thick, and densely packed [11].

VITAMINS, GROWTH SUBSTANCES, AND INHIBITORS • Many lichen fungi are
partially or wholly deficient for biotin and thiamine [7, 11, 112, 129, 179,
208, 302] (Figure 28). Whether these deficiencies exist during the lichen-

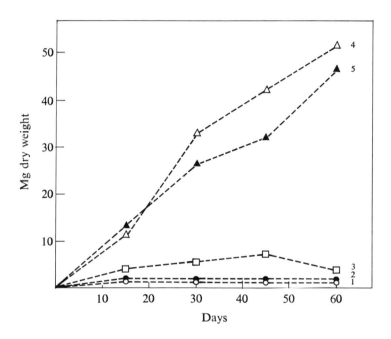

FIGURE 28. Growth curves of the mycobiont *Acarospora fuscata* in glucose-
asparagine vitamin supplement media. 1. no vitamins added. 2. thiamine
added. 3. biotin added. 4. thiamine and biotin added. 5. thiamine, biotin,
inositol, and pyridoxine added. From Ahmadjian, 1961 [7].

ized states of these fungi is not known. Studies of vitamin nutrition require
careful experimental technique in order to avoid "carry-over" of these compounds from the stock medium on which the fungi have grown to the test
medium. Trace amounts of vitamins can induce strong growth, so that in
investigations of this type care must be taken to insure that materials introduced to a medium do not carry contaminant vitamins. One procedure
is as follows: A mycobiont is grown in a glucose-asparagine-minerals liquid
medium (Appendix) until a quantity of fungal material has developed.

The fungus is filtered, washed with sterile distilled water, and inoculated into a similar medium but without added vitamins. After one week the fungus is filtered, washed several times with distilled water, and placed with water into a blender. Blending for ten to fifteen seconds generally will fragment most fungal material thoroughly. Equal portions (one ml) of this suspension are then pipetted into individual test flasks. The fungal fragments tend to rise to the surface of the water, so that to maintain a uniform distribution during the period of inoculation, the mixture must be agitated briefly at periodic intervals by turning on the blender. Several samples of the inoculum are conserved in separate vials in order to obtain average dry weights of the inoculated material. The number of hyphal fragments in each ml of inoculum also can be calculated [108]. The culture media are prepared as follows: sugar and nitrogen sources are boiled first for a few minutes with activated charcoal (5 g/liter) to remove traces of contaminant vitamins. The mixture is filtered, and vitamins and other microelements then are added to make up different series. The media are dispensed into clean glass flasks and autoclaved (the sugar should be filter sterilized and added aseptically to the rest of the autoclaved, cooled media). The following five series are prepared [165]: 1. Basal medium (vitamin-free); 2. Basal medium with thiamine (100 μg/liter); 3. Basal medium with biotin (5 μg/liter); 4. Basal medium with thiamine and biotin; 5. Basal medium with thiamine, biotin, inositol (5 mg/liter), and pyridoxine (100 μg/liter). Dry weight determinations of growth are made at intervals of fifteen, thirty, forty-five, and sixty days. Each reading should represent an average of the growth in no less than five flasks. To obtain fungal dry weights, the contents of the culture flasks are poured onto previously dried and weighed filter pads (preferably of glass fibers) in a filtering device which removes the liquid. The fungal mycelium is washed with distilled water, and then the filter pads are dried for about twenty-four hours at 95C and weighed. Dry weights of the fungi are calculated by obtaining the difference between these weights and those of the dried filter pads. Weighing must be done immediately after the pads are removed from the oven. Dried samples which are exposed to air with a relative humidity of 50% can absorb 1.8 mg of moisture in one minute and 5.7 mg after five minutes [179].

Algal extracts have stimulated growth of lichen fungi but the specific reasons for the growth-promoting effect have not been investigated [129, 302].

Indoleacetic acid (4–16 mg/liter) inhibited the growth of lichen fungi [302], but gibberellic acid (5–100 mg/liter) did not influence growth [102, 133].

Growth Rate

The best method for determining growth of lichen fungi is by dry weight measurements of their filtered and washed mycelia. For nutritional studies this method gives the most precise and reproducible results. In experiments which require only a coarse, comparative evaluation colony sizes of mycobionts grown on agar for several months can be determined.

Growth rates of lichen fungi under cultural conditions are extremely variable, due in part to their different requirements for optimal growth. Some strains on solid media reach a colony size of only 1–2 mm in diameter after nine to twelve months [7], a growth rate comparable to what most mycobionts achieve when they are in their lichenized states [114]. The most rapid growers in culture are species of *Acarospora, Cladonia,* and *Sarcogyne.* In 25 ml of a synthetic, basal medium with biotin and thiamine and with KNO_3 as a nitrogen source, an *A. fuscata* mycobiont, beginning with an average inoculum of 0.6 mg/ml dry weight of fragmented mycelium, after seventy days at 19C attained a maximum mycelial dry weight of 66 mg [11]. *C. cristatella* under the same conditions, except with L-alanine as a nitrogen source, attained a dry weight yield of 125 mg after seventy days [11]. Growth of *A. fuscata* with amino acids (Figure 27) was considerably less than with KNO_3 [108]. Hale [112, 114] reported yields of 100–110 mg for *A. fuscata* and *S. similis* after 50–60 days in culture. Tomaselli [279] and Henriksson [129] reported average yields of 1 mg a day for *Lecidea steriza* and *Collema tenax.*

Factors Influencing Growth

TEMPERATURE • The temperature range for maximum growth of lichen fungi is 15–28C [7, 114, 129, 271]. Most forms develop optimally at 18–21C. Low temperatures are tolerated better than high temperatures. A *Lasallia papulosa* mycobiont withstood immersion into liquid nitrogen (−197C) while suspended in a liquid medium [179]. The fungus need not be in a dried state to withstand low temperatures. The opposite is true with high temperatures. Under moist conditions lichen fungi have a tolerance limit of about 30C. In a dried state, however, they can withstand temperatures up to 45C for weeks [271]. No special protective hyphal structures are formed.

pH • For most mycobionts the pH optimum lies between 4.5 and 7.4 [7, 112, 129, 271].

LIGHT • Continuous or intermittent artificial light does not influence the growth of lichen fungi in culture. There have been reports of growth inhibitions caused by direct sunlight but these were undoubtedly due to the elevated temperature which resulted from such exposures.

Lichen Substances

One major unsolved problem in lichenology is the failure of isolated mycobionts to produce in culture the same chemical compounds they produce in lichen associations. Only a few mycobionts can synthesize lichen substances when they are apart from their algal partners. *Candelariella vitellina* forms stictaurin [271], a mixture of pulvic anhydride and calycin, and species of *Caloplaca* and *Xanthoria* produce physcion (= parietin) [270, 271, 278]. When these fungi are grown on solid media, they produce crystals of these compounds over the surface of their colonies and surrounding agar. The greatest amounts of the compounds are formed on complex culture media such as malt-yeast extract agar. No isolated mycobiont has produced a depside or a depsidone, the most common classes of lichen metabolites. A report of a *Cladonia cristatella* mycobiont synthesizing usnic, didymic, and rhodocladonic acids in culture [60] was not confirmed by later investigations [11]. Isolated mycobionts have produced pigments and crystals, some of which could not be detected in the corresponding lichen thalli [11, 78]. A few of these substances revealed properties similar to known lichen substances, such as a compound formed by *Acarospora smaragdula* which resembled usnic acid [17]. Extracts of isolated lichen fungi have shown antibiotic activity [17, 134].

Earlier it was thought that all the so-called lichen acids were unique products, but some free-living fungi produce similar compounds. Several species of *Aspergillus* and *Penicillium* form physcion [178], and *Aspergillus nidulans* produces nidulin and nornidulan, which belong to the depsidone class [72].

The formation of unidentified crystals by several mycobionts was noted only after the cultures had been stored for three months at 5C (Figure 29). Low temperatures may play a role in the synthesis of some lichen compounds [10].

FIGURE 29. Unidentified crystals excreted by a *Lecidea atrocinera* mycobiont after a three-month incubation period at 5C. (100 x) From Ahmadjian, 1963 [10].

Genetic Studies

Lichen fungi in culture are poor organisms to use as genetic tools because of their slow growth and absence of asexual and sexual reproductive bodies. The few traits which they have are pigmentation and colony morphology, but these tend to vary with the culture conditions. In one study seven hundred single ascospore isolations of *Cladonia cristatella* were made [11]. The differences among these isolates even among those from one fruiting body were striking. There were wide variations in size, shape, and color of the fungal colonies, and in four cultures bright red crystals were formed on the surface of the colonies. Actually, when considered in light of the high degree of natural variation exhibited by species of *Cladonia* [22], the variability of this fungus is not surprising, and it indicates a sexual process which includes fusion of nuclei with different genetic traits. The sexual processes of lichen fungi in their lichenized states [30, 141, 163, 184, 185, 194, 250, 264], are similar to those of free-living ascomycetes [19, 41].

Lichens, for the most part, consist of ascomycetous fungi, and the fruits which they form are similar to those of free-living fungi which belong to this group. The ascospores within lichen fruiting structures are products of meiotic divisions. Like other ascomycetes, the diploid part of the life cycle of a lichen fungus is represented only by a zygote nucleus which soon undergoes meiosis. The factors which stimulate sexuality in lichen fungi are not known. Perhaps sexuality consists only of fusion of two female nuclei [250]. Such self-fertilization, however, would produce homogeneous populations among groups of lichens, which is not the case. If, then, there are nuclear exchanges between different individuals, how do they occur? The most logical method is by pycniospores. These small, variably shaped spores are produced in large quantities by lichens. They are contained in flask-shaped structures called pycnidia which are associated closely with the fruiting bodies. Pycnidia usually are immersed in a thallus, and their openings appear as brown or black dots scattered over the surface of a lichen [194]. Pycniospores may act as male gametes which fuse with the trichogyne, an extension of the ascogonium or female reproductive part of a lichen fungus. Ascogonia are buried within a thallus, and only their trichogynes protrude through the upper surface (Figure 30). When a thallus is soaked, the pycnidia swell and extrude their contents in gelatinous masses. The pycniospores within these masses are transported over the thallus surface across any thin film of water, and some spores become attached to the trichogynes. Although some of the later stages of development beyond this point have not been observed in lichens, they probably are similar to those of other Ascomycetes [19]—that is, the nucleus of a pycniospore migrates through the trichogyne to the base of the ascogonium where it pairs with the female nucleus. Both nuclei then divide and form numerous pairs. These nuclei migrate into ascogenous hyphae which proliferate from the ascogonium. Fusion of a nuclear pair occurs within certain cells of the ascogenous hyphae. These cells then enlarge to form asci, or the spore sacs. During this time the fusion nucleus undergoes meiosis to form four haploid nuclei, each of which divides mitotically to give a total of eight nuclei. A spore forms about each nucleus. Ascogonia and ascogenous hyphae have been observed in many lichens, but the pattern of nuclear behavior during this time of development has not been established.

Pycniospores of some lichens have germinated and given rise to typical mycobiont colonies [182]. The fact that they could germinate suggested to some investigators a strictly asexual role for these spores. More probably some pycniospores have a dual role as sexual or asexual spores. A few *Buellia* and *Cladonia* mycobionts form pycnidia and pycniospores in culture [11, 14] but their spores do not germinate.

Recent cultural investigations [14] with *Cladonia cristatella* mycobionts have succeeded in inducing the production of sexual structures (see Chapter 4, pp. 83–84 for experimental details.) The mycobionts formed apothecia (Figure 31) and numerous pycnidia (Figure 32). Sections of these artifi-

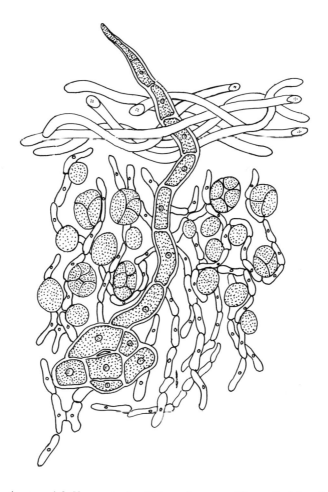

FIGURE 30. Ascogonial filament of a lichen fungus. The coiled basal end of the filament lies below the algal layer while the tip (trichogyne) of the filament extends above the surface of the lichen thallus.

cially synthesized young (3-month-old) fruiting bodies stained with haema-toxylin-eosin showed the presence of ascogonia and ascogenous hyphae (Figure 33) but not asci and spores. Pycniospores were extremely common and several instances were seen of a spore attached to a trichogyne-like structure, which extended out only a few microns from the surface of an apothecium (Figure 34).

Figure 31. Podetium and apothecia formed by the lichen fungus *Cladonia cristatella* in axenic culture. (40 x)

Chromosomes of lichen fungi, like those of many of their free-living relatives, are small, variable in shape and size, and generally bunched together. Some haploid chromosome numbers reported for lichen fungi are six to eight for several species of *Dermatocarpon*, five to six for *Collema*

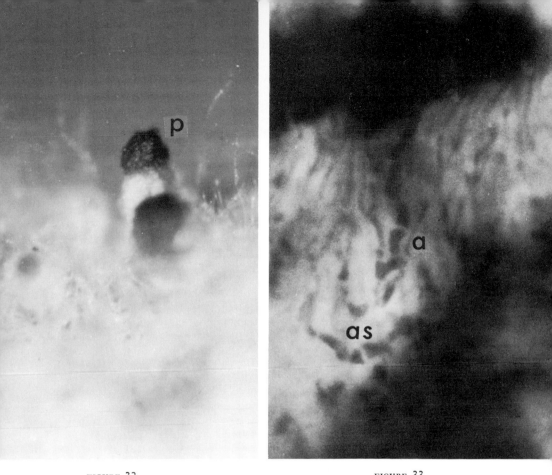

FIGURE 32   FIGURE 33

FIGURE 32. Pycnidium formed by the lichen fungus *Cladonia cristatella* in axenic culture. (40 x)

FIGURE 33. Section of a fruiting body (apothecium) formed by the lichen fungus *Cladonia cristatella* in axenic culture. Section stained with haematoxylin-eosin. a = ascogonial filament; as = ascogenous hyphae. (2000 x)

tenax, four for *Cladonia cristatella* and *Anaptychia ciliaris*, three for *Acarospora fuscata, Lecanora dispersa*, and a species of *Sarcogyne*, and two for *Lecidea crustulata* and several species of *Peltigera* [13, 20, 264]. In most cases mitotic stages were evident. In some instances centrosomes and spindles as well as polar asters were seen. Nuclei of lichen fungi are small, $2.2 \times 2.2 \mu$, and not clearly defined with stains. Chromosome sizes range from $0.3–2.2 \mu$. Cells are generally uninucleate, but older cells, many of them swollen, frequently contain two or three nuclei. Cytological studies of mycobionts can be made in their lichenized as well as isolated and cultured conditions. With the cultured mycobionts, young, actively growing mycelia are fragmented and placed in a fixative which consists of acetic acid, lactic acid, and 95% alcohol in a 1:1:6 mixture. The duration

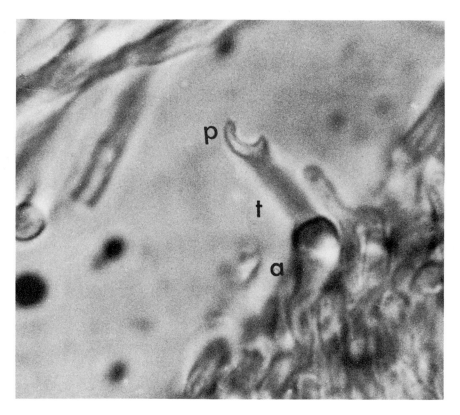

FIGURE 34. A pycniospore (p) attached to a trichogyne (t) which extends above the surface of a young apothecium (a) formed by the lichen fungus *Cladonia cristatella* in axenic culture. (4000 x) From "Artificial Reestablishment of the Lichen *Cladonia cristatella*," *Science*, 151 (January 14, 1966), 199–201. Copyright 1966 by the American Association for the Advancement of Science.

of fixation is variable and can range from two minutes to twenty-four hours, depending on the organism. Hyphae are stained by orcein which is prepared in the following manner: 100 mg of orcein are added to 5 ml of a mixture of 47 ml glacial acetic acid, 20 ml of a 1 ml lactic acid in a

24 ml H_2O solution, 5 ml 1N HCl, and 28 ml distilled water. The result-ing mixture is boiled for four minutes, cooled for one hour, and filtered. The stain is prepared fresh before each use. Chromosome observations can be made also on germ tubes. Spores of a lichen are allowed to dis-charge onto a film of water on a glass slide, which is kept then in a damp chamber until the germ tubes are several days old. The water film is allowed to dry, causing the spores to adhere firmly to the glass surface, and the slides are placed in fixative. When the slides are removed, the excess fixative is blotted away and stain is added to the areas of greatest spore concentration.

Nature of the
4 ❧ Lichen Association

~~~~~~

Origin of Lichens

There has been much speculation on the origin of lichens. At what stage in the earth's geological time scale the first lichen symbioses occurred is not known. The earliest recognized lichen fossil dates back to the Mesozoic epoch, with many more recorded from the Cenozoic [250]. The lack of fossils from earlier periods is probably a reflection of the poor preservation qualities of these associations. One assumption that can be made is that lichens were formed only after their component parts, fungi and algae, had undergone long periods of development. How and why the symbiosis first occurred are questions that cannot be answered precisely. However, in light of information obtained from experimental investigations, some reasonable conjectures can be made.

In natural habitats no plant lives alone. The competition for food and suitable substrates is so great that a number of different types of plants grow together. These associations invariably lead to consequences which may or may not be beneficial to one or more of the organisms. For example, one organism may excrete antibiotic substances which kill or retard the growth of its neighboring forms. Conversely, an organism may excrete organic compounds which would stimulate growth of other forms [209]. A lichen association may have started when fungi growing among algae became parasitic, perhaps in response to the diminishing nutrient supply of their substratum. When some lichen fungi are cultured under conditions of low nutrient supply, they tend to encircle almost any rounded object [4, 5, 8]. These intimate attachments were followed by penetrations of the algal cells. The penetrated algae were almost always killed, but continuous division of other cells maintained the population. Thus, the first primitive lichen developed—merely a granular, crustlike, fungal-algal association with no definite form or structure. It was not a unique association, since many other fungi developed parasitic relationships with other algae, particularly with marine forms and various land plants. When small particles of this primitive lichen were washed onto different substrates such as rock, where neither component could grow alone, only those forms persisted in which the parasitism was less severe, thereby allowing for survival of the alga. Under these conditions, which necessitated close cooperation between the organisms so that both could survive, parasitism gradually developed into mutualism, and fungus and alga became dependent on each other. Moreover, mutations which deprived either fungus or alga of the capacity to synthesize vital compounds such as vitamins made the association more permanent, if the deficient substances were provided by one of the organisms.

Drying also may have been a factor in the lichenization of fungal–algal associations. Dry conditions stimulate the fungus to form more intimate unions with the alga.

Many different fungi, mostly from the *Ascomycetes*, formed mutualistic relationships with algae. The types of algae which could be used were limited not only to those whose outer walls or sheaths could be penetrated but also to those which could survive the fungal attacks and demands [5]. Among the fungi natural selection favored strains with slow growth rates, since the rapid growers would destroy all the algal cells in their associations and bring about their own destruction.

As evolution progressed, the primitive crustose types, in response to environmental conditions, gave rise to more definite forms such as foliose or leaflike shapes and fruticose or stalked shapes in which the algae were concentrated into distinct layers. Lichen thalli were well designed for the harsh conditions of sun, wind, snow, and ice, and the associations began to colonize habitats such as sunbaked desert rocks and windswept alpine peaks where few other forms of life could survive.

This picture of lichen evolution is simple and speculative, but it is the best that can be done with our present state of knowledge.

One might consider whether in present times and under natural conditions lichens can arise *de novo* from separate fungi and algae. Some investigators propose that the principal means of lichen dispersal is by vegetative structures, such as small thallus fragments [283] and soredia which are easily distributed by wind [46], rain, and animals (Figure 35). Some workers consider these as the only means of propagation. The first proposal undoubtedly is true, since any one of the large numbers of these vegetative structures under proper conditions can produce a new lichen; but the second consideration is incorrect, because it assumes that the spores produced by lichen fungi are without function. It is inconceivable that some of the incalculable number of spores which are disseminated from lichen fruits do not unite with suitable algae to form a *composite plant*. In fact, for many lichens which lack vegetative dispersal units and are not readily fragmented, this must be the only means by which they are distributed. We do not know clearly the fate of the discharged lichen spores under natural conditions, but in recent laboratory experiments [14] with *Cladonia cristatella* the ascospores gave rise to fungal colonies, which gave rise not only to sexual structures but also, with the alga, formed distinct lichen structures such as squamules and soredia. These experiments illustrated that the lichen association can originate from the separate fungus and alga, and that the ascospores are functional in the reestablishment of the symbiosis.

A popular image has been that after the ascospores are discharged they germinate, and if the young fungal filaments do not link up with a suitable algal type within a short period of time, they perish. This is probably not the case for many lichens. Lichen fungi are extremely hardy, and it is likely that they can survive and grow in a saprophytic manner for long periods of time without algae [241]. Some may even survive on rock surfaces with only traces of organic nutrients. Many spores, of course, are carried to areas where free-living algae are present. Under these circumstances the young fungi will form intimate contacts with algal cells and use them for nutrients if the alga is sensitive to the fungal attack. There is no evidence to indicate that these fungi actively seek out a suitable algal partner. It is a question of which algal type can withstand the encroachments and subsequent conditions which a particular fungus imposes on it [5]. We might in a popular sense consider these unions as "trial marriages." The frequency of these trial unions, because of the enormous

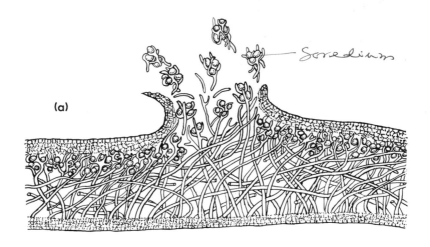

Soredium

(a)

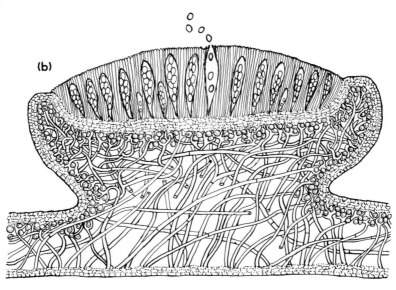

(b)

FIGURE 35. (a) Vegetative propagation is the surest means by which lichens multiply. One such method is by the breaking off of particles, or soredia, composed of fungal hyphae and algae. (b) Fruiting bodies, the typical structures of sexual reproduction in fungi, are found in most lichens. Within each fruiting body there are a large number of bulbous sacs (asci) containing the reproductive cells or spores. Even when the fruiting body has algal cells in its margin, as in this case, the spores are purely fungal. From "The Fungi of Lichens," V. Ahmadjian. Copyright © 1963 by _Scientific American, Inc._ All rights reserved.

production of spores, obviously is high. Microscopic examination of almost any algal cover of tree bark will show fungal hyphae, some of which have formed close attachments to algal cells [5, 207]. Many of these hyphae are undoubtedly those derived from lichen fungal spores. Once initial associations have been made with tolerant algae (even with one cell), development proceeds further to form a lichen [240]. In some instances the algae (*Trebouxia*) which are found in lichens are not abundant outside of the association, but they do occur in small, isolated groups among other algae. Perhaps the same characteristics which make them suitable as fungal partners place them at a disadvantage in the free-living state.

Physical Nature of the Lichen Symbiosis

The contacts between lichen symbionts can be observed easily when small pieces of a thallus are placed in a drop of water, fragmented between two glass slides, and the resulting suspension is examined microscopically. The union is so close that this drastic treatment does not separate the components completely. Fungal hyphae form a close network around the algal cells and in many instances embed them in a tissuelike mass of cells. Most lichens show some degree of penetration of their phycobiont's cells by fungal haustoria [105] (Figure 36). Among lichens without well-defined thalli, penetrations are mostly of the intracellular type (Figure 37). In these cases, haustoria appear to penetrate the algal protoplast and often extend to the middle of a cell [201, 281]. The cell wall of a haustorium remains intact, but it is thinner than the wall of a hypha which is outside the algal cell. Electron microscopy studies of a few lichens have not defined clearly whether the unit membrane of an algal protoplast is penetrated or whether it invaginates to produce a sheath around a haustorium [13]. The haustoria seem to penetrate the algal cell walls largely by a mechanical action. The cell walls are pushed in and ruptured by the haustoria, which are sheathed in a collarlike manner by the broken algal wall [13]. There is no encapsulation surrounding a haustorium. The haustoria occupy an invagination of the algal chloroplast.

Haustoria are slender and straight during the early stages of penetration but later their tips become swollen, thereby increasing their area for absorption. Frequently a haustorium is deflected to one side or broken because of the resistance of a chloroplast [201]. A maximum number of five haustoria in one algal cell has been reported [201, 281]. The haustoria

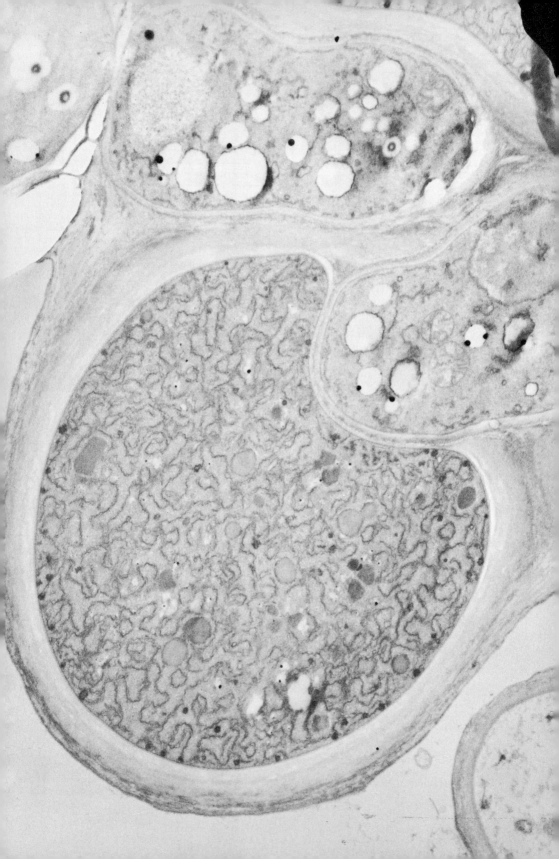

seem in some lichens to destroy the algal cells and absorb their protoplasts [201]. In other lichens, however, the haustoria seem to stimulate divisions of the algae and later infect the daughter cells [105].

Lichens with well-defined thalli have mostly the intramembranous type of haustorium. This type of haustorium penetrates the algal cell wall but does not extend into the protoplast [201, 281]. Electron micrographs of *Cladonia cristatella* and a *Lecidea* sp. show details of this type of penetration [183] (Figure 38). Lichens with thalli intermediate between poorly-defined and well-defined types show obvious transitions in the types of haustoria [201]. A few lichens, e.g. *Peltigera aphthosa*, which have *Coccomyxa* as a phycobiont, do not have haustoria. The cell walls of both symbionts, however, are very thin and probably allow for an adequate transport of organic materials [38, 201].

Some lichens show fluctuations in the frequency of haustoria [229]. Whether this is true of all lichens is not known. In species of *Collema* the fluctuations appear to be seasonal in that during most of the year contacts between the symbionts are very loose, but in autumn the fungus penetrates and destroys a number of algal cells [281, 282].

Tests of the chemical nature of the cell walls of algal symbionts have been made mostly with staining reagents. *Trebouxia* phycobionts give positive cellulose reactions to stains such as zinc-chloro-iodide [2]. In one study, however, two strains of *Trebouxia* which had positive stain reactions gave negative results—i.e., cellulose was not detected with X ray diffraction methods [98].

Lichenlike Associations

A number of fungi grow and produce fruiting bodies on the surface of lichen thalli. Many of these fungi have fruits which are similar to or identical with those of lichens—that is, they are perennial, tough, and leathery. The hyphae of these fungi penetrate the lichen thalli and form intimate unions with cells of the algal symbiont. These fungi occupy an intermediate position between lichens and free-living fungi. They have been called parasymbionts or lichen parasites, depending on whether or not they cause noticeable harm to the algae [75, 194]. In general, these forms

FIGURE 36. (opposite) *Heppia lutosa*: an electron micrograph showing a cell of the phycobiont (*Scytonema*) and a haustorium of the fungal partner. (11,000 x)

grow on lichens only, and it is not clear whether they represent free-living fungi which are in the early stages of lichenization, or known lichens in the late stages of delichenization, or lichen fungi which under the competitive conditions of a foreign thallus produce fruiting bodies but not thalli.

Another small group of fungi, sometimes called facultative lichens, can live saprophytically without algae and also form lichenized unions [75, 86]. Examples such as these illustrate that a lichen is not a stable association and that both partners under certain environmental conditions can revert

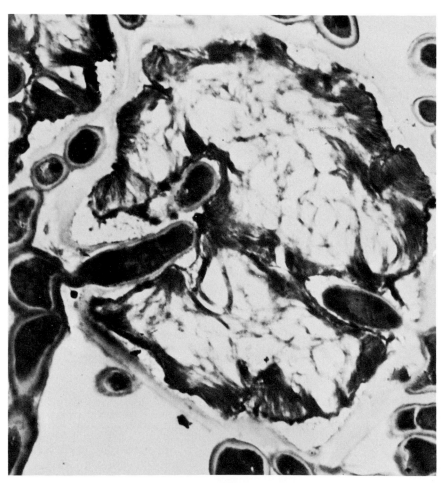

FIGURE 37. *Maronella laricina:* an electron micrograph showing a cell of the phycobiont (*Myrmecia*) and intracellular haustoria of the fungal partner. (10,000 x) From Ahmadjian, 1966 [13].

to free-living states. Critical studies may show that many other fungi which form lichens are able to live saprophytically in a free-living condition before joining with algae to form *composite plants.*

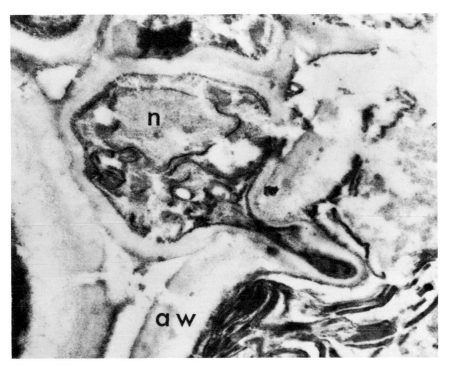

FIGURE 38. *Cladonia cristatella:* an electron micrograph showing the outer margin of a phycobiont (*Trebouxia*) cell and an intercellular haustorium of the fungal partner. aw = algal cell wall; n = nucleus of fungal cell. (30,000 x) From Moore and McAlear, 1960 [183].

Some lichenlike associations consist of filamentous algae which are enveloped by fungal hyphae (Figure 39). These associations are usually permanent but the fungus does not undergo a morphological differentiation and does not become the predominant partner [143, 145]. A few of these associations achieve a morphological integrity, perhaps by means of a chemical influence by the fungus.

The occurrence of lichenlike associations is not surprising. The evolution of lichens must have occurred from a broadly based series of fungal–algal associations. It would be reasonable to assume that not all of these

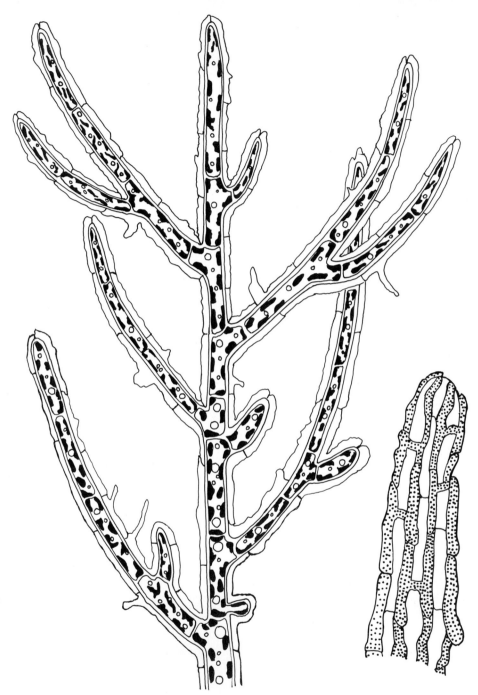

FIGURE 39. *Coenogonium*: a lichenlike association of *Trentepohlia* and fungus.

associations developed into lichens, that is, not all fungi were capable of undergoing a morphological differentiation, and that transitional stages between loose fungal–algal relationships and highly structured lichen thalli exist. Lichenlike associations between myxomycetes and *Streptomyces* with the green alga *Chlorella* have been induced artificially in culture [161a].

A lichen thallus is a substrate on which a wide variety of organisms grow. The most prevalent types are bacteria, as one can readily ascertain when culture investigations are attempted. Because of the frequent isolation from many lichens of the nitrogen-fixing bacterium *Azotobacter*, the possibility of regarding lichen associations as multiple mutualistic symbioses has been considered [236]. There is no direct evidence, however, which shows the contribution *Azotobacter* may make to a lichen symbiosis [45, 236]. Many different organisms, such as yeasts, bacteria, fungi, algae, and protozoans, grow on or even within a lichen thallus, and some probably contribute to the lichen and receive usable materials from it. If one defines a lichen association solely from a physiological point of view, then these associations could be considered as multiple, mutualistic symbioses.

Physiology of the Lichen Symbiosis ✓

The type of physiological interplay which exists between lichen symbionts has been discussed ever since the dual nature of these associations was discovered. The most widely accepted theory is that the phycobiont, because of its photosynthetic capabilities, provides its fungal partner with organic compounds while the mycobiont provides the alga with water, minerals, and protection from desiccation and high light intensities. There is direct experimental evidence to support parts of this theory. The movement of organic compounds from alga to fungus has been demonstrated in *Peltigera polydactyla*, a lichen with *Nostoc* as phycobiont, by means of sodium bicarbonate ($NaHCO_3$) labeled with C^{14} [254, 258]. Discs were cut from a thallus and floated on an aqueous solution of the labeled compound. The discs were illuminated for eight hours and then kept in darkness for seven hours. Periodically, discs were removed, and after the algal and medullary layers were separated by dissection (Table 2), the amount of C^{14} present in each layer was determined. Since all the radioactive bicarbonate was removed from the extracts of these layers before C^{14} determination, the C^{14} which remained was that which had been incorporated into organic compounds. Much of the C^{14} fixed during photo-

TABLE 2

Physiological Properties of Algal Zones and Medullae of *Peltigera polydactyla* after Separation by Dissection
From D. C. Smith, 1963 [256].

(Data calculated as mean values for normal thalli.)

| | Dry wt. per cm.[2] thallus mg. | Composition per 100 mg. dry weight | | | | Absorption from 5 mM solutions (per 100 mg. dry wt./24 hr. at 20°.)[4] | | | Oxygen uptake per 100 mg. dry wt. at 20°[7] µl./hr. |
| | | N[1] mg. | Carbohydrate[2] mg. | | Saturated water content mg. | Glucose[5] mg. | Asparagine mg. N | Phosphate[6] mg. P | |
			Sol.[3]	Insol.					
Algal zones →	3·6	4·5	7·6	18·8	305	23·4	1·7	1·11	121
Medullae →	2·3	2·5	4·0	24·8	375	11·8	1·4	0·86	70

Notes:
1 Measured in November, when the nitrogen content of thallus is at its highest.
2 Measured in May-June, just after season of maximum carbohydrate content.
3 Does not include sugar alcohols.
4 Aqueous solutions, and pH maintained at 5·6–5·8 by 10 mM phthalate buffer.
5 Total absorption by tissue zones is 23% less than undissected controls.
6 Total absorption by tissue zones is 17% less than undissected controls.
7 Total oxygen uptake by tissue zones is 56% greater than undissected controls.

From *Symbiotic Associations*, Nutman and Mosse (eds.) (London: Cambridge University Press), 36.

Transverse section of the thallus

25 µ — Upper cortex
50 µ — Algal layer
Dissection
400 µ — Medulla

Algal zones
Medullae

synthesis appeared in the sugar alcohol mannitol.   It was not clear whether or not this compound was the first photosynthetic product or an early derivative [257].   Fixation of labeled carbon in control discs which were kept in darkness varied from 4.8–9.4% of the light fixation values.   The labeled organic compounds appeared first in the algal layer and later in the medulla, an area composed solely of fungal hyphae.   Movement of these compounds to the medulla occurred within fifteen minutes [258] (Figure 40), presumably through hyphae which connected algal cells with the medullary zone.   It is possible that some movement of materials between the symbionts took place by diffusion and subsequent absorption by fungal hyphae.   A *Nostoc* phycobiont has been shown to excrete large amounts of organic compounds into its culture medium [124, 125, 128].

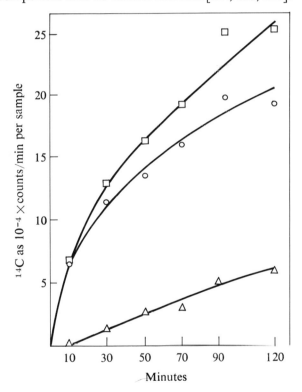

FIGURE 40.   Movement of photosynthetic products from algal layer (O) to medulla (Δ) in *Peltigera polydactyla* discs (total = □). Sample size ten discs; 200 mg NaHC^{14}O$_3$ per ml; pH 6.5; light intensity 425 ft.c.; temperature 20C.   Results corrected for dark fixation. From Smith and Drew, 1965 [258].

There is evidence [8] which suggests that the flow of organic materials from alga to fungus takes place in other lichens with green algae as phycobionts. Whether the green lichen algae, especially *Trebouxia*, excrete as much organic material as blue-green algae or other related green algae is not known. However, the intimate contacts which lichen fungi make with these phycobionts would indicate that the mycobionts play a more active role by absorbing materials directly from within the algal cells.

The evidence that under natural conditions mycobionts provide their algal partners with water and minerals is found in investigations which have demonstrated the efficient absorption properties of fungal hyphae [255] and the chelating powers of lichen acids [226]. Some experimentation has showed that a mycobiont protected its algal partner from drying, but the protection was slight and present only when the drying conditions were not severe [208]. There is evidence that a mycobiont protects its phycobiont from high light intensities [8]. The fungal cells which make up the upper cortex of a thallus shield the algae from light intensities which ordinarily would be lethal.

Cultural studies of isolated symbionts have provided information which allows for a detailed analysis of a lichen association, although, from a cautionary view, it must be stated that such information may not reflect entirely what occurs under the natural conditions of a symbiosis.

The finding that many mycobionts are deficient for biotin and thiamine and that some phycobionts excrete these vitamins suggests one relationship. Compounds such as ascorbic acid, which stimulated the photosynthetic rates of isolated phycobionts [208], may play a similar role in a lichen thallus. Although ascorbic acid is not produced by isolated mycobionts, it has been found in lichens, and a similar stimulatory effect could be caused by other substances such as lichen acids or pigments. In view of the reduced amount of light which reaches an algal layer, it is a possibility.

An interesting aspect of the symbiosis is whether or not the fungus has a direct influence through chemical intermediates on the metabolism of its algal partner. It seems unlikely that a flow of materials between the partners occurs at a uniform rate throughout the growth season. Several of the fungal processes such as growth, fruit formation, and spore discharge are more prevalent during certain times of the year. Since some of these activities would require increased amounts of food materials, at these times the mycobiont could stimulate the metabolic rates of its algal symbiont and thereby increase the flow of organic materials. One way in which this stimulation could occur is as follows: many isolated mycobionts produce urease [13], an enzyme which is present also in naturally occurring lichens

Arginine ⟶ ornithine + urea

[181]. Urease speeds the hydrolysis of urea to ammonia and carbon dioxide, both of which can have a marked influence on the metabolism of the algae. Ammonium nitrogen induces rapid respiration and carbohydrate breakdown in nitrogen-starved *Chlorella* [268], an alga which has been found as a lichen symbiont. As it seems likely that lichen algae would be nitrogen-starved at various times of the year, under the conditions and competition imposed upon them by their fungal partners, such a stimulatory effect by ammonia could occur within a thallus as well. Variation in total nitrogen content has been observed with *Peltigera polydactyla* thalli, with the lowest values recorded for March and October [254]. The dry weights and carbohydrate contents of these thalli also reached their lowest values in early spring and late fall. On the other hand, the highest levels of metabolic activity occurred each year from March–June and from October–December. This seasonal pattern coincides with peak periods of a mycobiont's activities. For example, the percentage of spore discharge and germination in many lichens is greatest in spring and fall which are peak periods also for podetial formation by *Cladonia coniocraea* [23]. The most active periods of growth in some lichens have been shown to occur during seasons of high humidity and cool temperatures, such as in the spring and fall [57, 199, 221].

The carbon dioxide released from urea hydrolysis would increase photosynthesis of the alga and thus prevent a lethal drain.

Urea occurs commonly among fungi and other plants [93], and there is reason to assume that it is present within lichen thalli, either introduced from external sources or more probably formed by mycobionts from a process such as breakdown of the amino acid arginine, which would yield a molecule of urea and one of ornithine. When lichen fungi were grown in a culture medium that contained arginine, urea was produced [16]. Moreover, under natural conditions the presence of amino nitrogen in lichen-stabilized crusts has been reported [247]. These nitrogenous compounds are released from dead cells of both symbionts and probably epiphytic organisms as well and accumulate in this crust. They may be either mincralized and distributed with soil water or, more likely, absorbed by the living cells of the thallus. Urea can be stored by fungi, and when growth conditions are favorable it can be used as a source of nitrogen, by both symbionts in the case of lichens, and also be split to form ammonia and carbon dioxide. Fungi may contain urea and produce urease simultaneously [93]. Urea also may function in increasing the permeability of the algal cells, a property which it has with other plants [138]. This proposal is speculative in several respects, but it does illustrate the type of interplay which may exist between the symbionts. It is possible that the seasonal responses of a mycobiont are supported by nutrient material which accumulates either through an excess of photosynthetic products or through absorption of substances from the substrate and is stored in the medulla. Studies on polysaccharide distribution in *Peltigera polydactyla* showed that the medulla contained 50% more polysaccharide than the algal layer, which indicates that storage areas may exist within a lichen thallus [254, 257]. Many questions remain unanswered in our understanding of the physiological relationships of a lichen symbiosis.

Once the dual nature of a lichen had been established beyond doubt, the controversy moved to an interpretation of its nature [85, 86]. Does a lichen represent a mutualistic or parasitic association? Proponents of both sides marshaled strong arguments, but the controversy persists, mainly because the many types of lichenized unions defy *all or none* definitions. To say that all lichens are mutualistic is as wrong as saying that all are parasitic. There are examples of both types of associations among lichens, and in some cases the two conditions may exist concurrently within the same thallus. In some *Collema* lichens the fungal hyphae periodically destroy certain parts of the algal colony while living mutualistically with the rest [282]. Moreover, neither condition need be permanent and one can change easily to the other [104, 276]. Advocates of mutualism point to the exchange of materials between partners, the seemingly healthy existence of algal cells within a thallus, and the fact that in many instances lichens grow in areas where neither component could survive alone. Those who propose parasitism use for their main argument the haustorial penetrations of algal cells and the lack of any real benefit which an alga receives from its fungal partner—that is, the receipt of something which it ordinarily could not obtain in the free-living state. More recent views speak of a controlled parasitism where the alga survives but nonetheless is drained of its food reserves [114, 152, 153]. In this respect, it is more probable to say that the parasitism is so gradual that one or several new generations of algal cells mature before the older, infected ones succumb [197]. The nature of lichen symbioses must be viewed as being varied and varying, as might be expected among a class of organisms with a polyphyletic origin.

Specificity of the Algal Symbiont

Interest in the relationships between lichen fungi and algae extends also to the question of how specific the symbionts are to each other. For a long time it was concluded that lichen fungi were highly specific with regard to their algal partners, and that each lichen contained a morphologically or physiologically distinctive alga [61, 140, 291]. If this theory of extreme specificity were true, one would expect a widespread distribution of different types of free-living algae which were capable of forming lichenized associations, in order that the fungal spores could find appropriate partners to form thalli identical with those of their parent associations. Proponents of the specificity theory went further to state that even individuals of one lichen species growing in different areas could have different algal types. As experimental evidence accumulated, however, it became clear that the fungi were not specific to their algal partners. For example, thalli of unrelated lichens such as *Chaenotheca chrysocephala* and *Cladonia furcata* had identical *Trebouxia* phycobionts, as did specimens of *Cyphelium inquinans* f. *minor* and *Cladonia fimbriata* [214] and species of *Cladonia* and *Stereocaulon* [3]. The *Trebouxia* symbionts from thalli of *Buellia punctata* and *Xanthoria parietina* were identical not only in their morphology but also in certain physiological traits such as growth rate, temperature optimum, and nutrition [6]. Perhaps the best example is *Myrmecia biatorellae*. This alga has been found as a symbiont in an aquatic lichen, *Verrucaria submersa*, and a terrestrial one, *Dermatocarpon velebiticum*, as well as in eight other species of lichens [105]. Individuals of one lichen collected from different localities, and even from the same locality, may have as a phycobiont strikingly different species of an algal genus [16], and in some cases a single thallus may contain several types of algae. This latter condition is illustrated by cephalodia, structures which appear on the surface of many lichens and are composed of blue-green algae lichenized by the same fungus which forms the main thallus with green algae. In some lichens, such as *Solorina*, blue-green and green algae form distinct layers within one thallus. Also, one fungus may form identical associations with different algae. *Lobaria pulmonaria* and *Lobaria retigera* are lichens which are morphologically indistinguishable, except that the former has a green phycobiont (*Coccomyxa*) and the latter, a blue-green phycobiont (*Nostoc*) [26].

There is sufficient experimental evidence to allow for the generalization that lichen fungi are not specific to their algal components. The lichenization of a single alga by different fungi [5] or, conversely, the lichenization of different algae by one fungus [218] is probably very common. If an alga can survive in one lichen association, there is no reason why it could not survive in others where the conditions imposed upon it might be similar. Study of the problem of algal specificity involves considerable isolation and culture work and should deal with the total algal population within a lichen rather than with a small group of randomly isolated cells. Since the main mode of lichen dissemination is by means of vegetative structures, one would expect to find in any given area a remarkable uniformity of algal types among the members of one lichen species. The fact that different algae are found in individuals of one lichen type supports the view that spores dispersed from lichen thalli may be capable of forming the associations.

Synthesis Experiments

Many investigators have attempted to reestablish a lichen association beginning with the separate symbionts. Their attempts were not completely successful, but they did help to determine the conditions under which synthesis will occur [8, 179, 296]. Available evidence, which is based on laboratory and field observations, indicates that lichen-forming fungi and algae are not obligate symbionts and that under suitable conditions for growth each organism develops independently. Appropriate fungi and algae must be forced into forming lichen unions. Factors which promote independent growth of either or both organisms not only prevent synthesis but also cause separation of established associations. If a lichen is taken from its natural habitat to a laboratory and kept under prolonged conditions of moisture, light, or nutrient supply, it will soon dissociate into separate growths of the partners. These separations occur even in nature depending on the environmental conditions. Lichen development is a continuous balanced growth between the fungus and its algal partner [12, 96, 239, 275].

Reestablishment of a lichen association can be accomplished under laboratory conditions. One experimental procedure, which achieved a partial synthesis and was applied to the lichen *Acarospora fuscata* [8, 10], was as follows: pieces of the colonies of both symbionts were washed free of nutrient medium, placed into a blender along with a small amount of distilled water, and fragmented for about fifteen seconds. The resulting mixture of algal cells and fungal hyphae was pipetted into flasks which contained a purified agar medium without supplements. The cultures were incubated at 20C and 30–50 ft.c. of illumination. Microscopic examination of the cultures was made at periodic intervals by scraping some of the growth off the agar surface. Initial contacts between the symbionts were seen ten days after inoculation of the flasks (Figure 41). After thirty days the fungal hyphae which enveloped the algal cells proliferated into small, irregular-shaped cells that formed a compact tissuelike mass called a pseudoparenchyma (= paraplectenchyma) (Figure 42). This tissue was formed only by hyphae which were in contact with algal cells, perhaps in response to the configuration of the enveloped cells or nutrient materials excreted by these algae. This stage of development represents the second

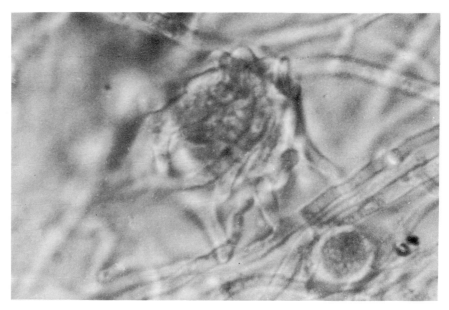

FIGURE 41. Surface view of a *Trebouxia* cell enveloped by fungal hyphae. An early stage in the artificial reestablishment of the lichen *Acarospora fuscata*. (2400 x) From "Investigations on Lichen Synthesis," V. Ahmadjian, *American Journal of Botany*, 49 (1962), 280.

step in lichen synthesis, the first being the envelopment of algal cells by fungal hyphae. The time it took for the formation of pseudoparenchyma around the algal cells was shortened in some cases by adding vitamins such as biotin and thiamine to the agar, or by keeping both symbionts in distilled water for approximately two to three weeks prior to the inoculation. Once the fungal tissue had formed around the algal cells, the two components behaved as a lichenized unit at least in terms of the functional relationships between the symbionts. The pseudoparenchyma cells produced a water-soluble pigment which was similar to one formed by the mycobiont in culture. The pigment was synthesized only when the fungus was supplied with adequate levels of organic nutrients. Since, in the synthesis cultures, pigment was formed only by the pseudoparenchyma cells, it was assumed that the fungal cells were receiving organic compounds from the alga [13]. After several months the algae not enclosed in tissue had disintegrated or turned yellow. The algal cells enveloped in fungal tissue, however, re-

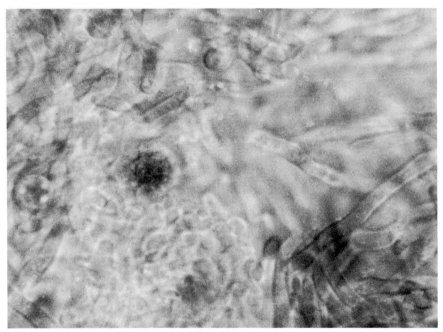

FIGURE 42. Several *Trebouxia* cells enveloped in pseudoparenchyma tissue formed by the fungus. A later stage in the artificial reestablishment of the lichen *Acarospora fuscata*. (2400 x) From "Investigations on Lichen Synthesis," V. Ahmadjian, *American Journal of Botany*, 49 (1962), 280.

mained bright green and showed various division stages which indicated that the algae had obtained nutrient materials from the fungus. The fungus probably obtained these substances through enzymatic breakdown of the extruded cell contents of the dead algae, including those fragmented by the blender. After they divided a few times, the enveloped algal cells retained sizes comparable to those of algal cells within a lichen thallus. The pseudoparenchyma units continued to develop even after one year of culture and the beginning of further differentiation into the various thallus layers was seen. The cultures, however, did not progress beyond these preliminary stages.

The third step in lichen synthesis, the formation of a mature thallus, required conditions in addition to a nutrient poor substrate. One of the most important conditions was that of drying [14]. This was demonstrated by another experiment. The two symbionts were fragmented together in a blender, and the mixture cultured for several months on an organic nutrient agar medium. The resulting growth was scraped from the agar surface and placed onto sterilized rock fragments from which thalli of the natural lichen had been removed. The rocks were placed in petri dishes and kept under the same conditions of incubation described above. Periodic wetting and drying was achieved by alternating the humidity of the incubator, flooding the petri dish with water, which was then removed after several days, or wetting the culture directly with water. Under these conditions lichenization proceeded rapidly, and after several months some of the cultures resembled lichen thalli, both macroscopically and microscopically. The pigmentation of the naturally occurring thallus was not duplicated in the artificial form. The pigments may have developed in response to a fluctuation of other conditions such as temperature and light intensity.

The fourth and final stage of lichen synthesis—that is, the formation of fruiting bodies, also was achieved in laboratory culture [14]. The experimental procedure for the fourth stage [14], was as follows: spores from the lichen's (*Cladonia cristatella*) fruiting bodies were allowed to fall onto an agar medium, either soil-extract or malt-yeast extract agar, in 250 ml erlenmeyer flasks, each of which contained a piece of rotted wood (e.g. apple, maple), which was part of the original substrate from which the test lichens were collected. The wood fragment was placed either horizontally on the bottom of the flask or in a slanted position. The flask with the wood was autoclaved and kept for twenty-four hours at 37C to allow for germination of any heat resistant spores of contaminant organisms. Medium then was added to the flask, at a level which would not fully cover the surface of the wood, and the flask was autoclaved again. Spore discharge into the flasks was achieved by placing washed apothecia onto petri dish covers and placing these covers over the mouths of the flasks. The covers were kept in this position for as long as two days, or until a sufficient spore discharge was obtained. One of the covers with apothecia was placed over the bottom of a petri dish filled with agar, as a means of determining the relative amount of spore discharge from the population of lichen which was being used. The covers on the flasks were replaced with sterile cotton plugs and incubation was at 20C. After germination of the spores—which could be determined by examination of the control petri dish—a suspension of a fresh liquid culture of *Trebouxia erici* (symbiont of *Cladonia cristatella*) was added to the flasks. The flasks were incubated under constant illumination at 100 ft.c. In a few weeks the alga formed a continuous cover over the medium, and growth was heavy also on the wood. After a few months the fungus formed colonies which grew up through the algal cover. As the cultures slowly dried—and this could be seen by the shrinkage of the agar—the fungi formed reproductive structures. These reproductive structures included numerous pycnidia, which were the first to appear, and which contained numerous pycniospores that were exuded in gelatinous strings. Both pycnidia and spores were identical to those found in the natural associations. Apothecia appeared later and were not as common as pycnidia: they formed directly on a colony, usually in clusters of a dozen or more (Figure 43) or they were produced singly on small podetia which emerged from the colony (see Figure 31). The apothecia contained the typical reproductive tissues as well as distinct ascogonial filaments and ascogenous hyphae. Asci were not seen in these young fruits. The development of these reproductive structures in culture was similar to that of a related lichen, *Cladonia floerkeana*, in nature [164].

FIGURE 43. Cluster of sessile apothecia formed on a colony of the lichen fungus *Cladonia cristatella* in axenic culture. (40 x)

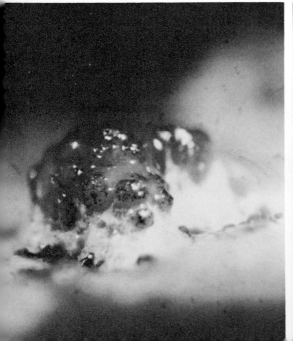

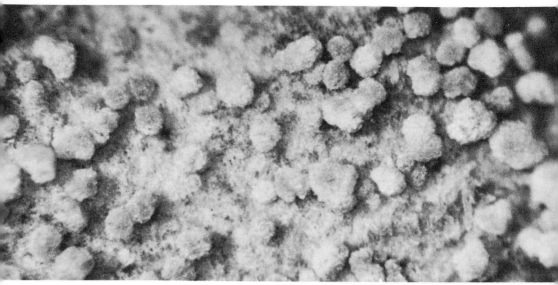

FIGURE 44. Soredia formed on a colony of the lichen fungus *Cladonia crista-tella* in axenic culture. (40 x)

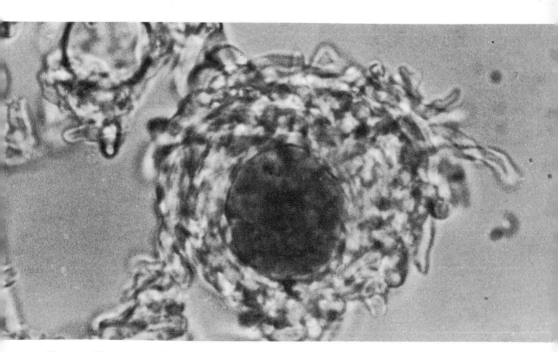

FIGURE 45. A soredium formed by the lichen fungus *Cladonia cristatella* in axenic culture. (2000 x)

Both apothecia and pycnidia were formed by the fungus in the absence of the alga, indicating that the fruiting stage of a lichen fungus is not obligately dependent on the attainment of the symbiotic state. The stimulus for the formation of the reproductive structures was the slow drying of the cultures.

It was found further [14] that *C. cristatella* mycobionts which had been in culture for several years did not form reproductive structures under the same experimental conditions. They did, however, form soredia (Figures 44, 45) and squamules in response to the joint effect of slow drying and nutrient-poor conditions. Other species of *Cladonia* mycobionts have formed podetial-like structures in culture [8] (Figure 46) but they lost their ability to form these structures after being in culture for several months.

The information obtained from lichen synthesis investigations can be summarized as follows: 1. The most important conditions for the establishment of lichen associations are nutrient-poor substrates and slow drying (or alternate drying and wetting); 2. Spores of a lichen fungus are capable of reestablishing lichen unions in culture; 3. The fungal symbiont can fruit in the absence of its algal partner; 4. A mycobiont in culture loses its ability to fruit but can still form the lichenized state with algae.

FIGURE 46. (opposite) Podetium produced by the lichen fungus *Cladonia piedmontensis* in axenic culture. (90 x)

age of substrate in years is plotted against the dry weight of the lichen. Slopes of the resulting lines will indicate relative growth rates [200].

Lichens do not grow at uniform annual rates. Their yearly increments vary considerably according to the moisture and temperature conditions of their environment. Periods of high humidity and cool temperatures are best for lichen development [57, 221], while warm, dry summers and winters either inhibit completely or slow their growth. Variable growth rates exist even among different lobes or areas of one thallus [110, 168]. The speed of growth may also vary with the age of a thallus [97, 168, 199]. Young thalli generally grow more rapidly than older ones [221], although several investigators have found the opposite to be true with some lichens [113, 199] and one has found no difference in growth between young (= small) and old (= large) thalli [48]. Lichens have been described whose size and general appearance remained unchanged for periods of twenty years [97]. It is difficult to understand why there should be a decline or cessation of radial increase, because the outer parts of a thallus are always young in comparison to inner portions. Lichens should be able to grow indefinitely provided their margins are free. With crustose forms radial growth stops completely when one thallus meets another.

Although some lichens, such as arctic species of *Rhizocarpon* and *Lecidea,* are very durable and have ages estimated to range from 1000 to 4500 years [40], other forms, like *Peltigera* and *Umbilicaria,* may show remarkably rapid changes in growth and coverage of a particular area. One species of *Peltigera* which was observed to be very abundant in a certain region one year had disappeared completely by the following year [110]. Photographic studies of small plots of land, fences, stumps, and other substrates over periods of up to thirty-seven years have illustrated the changing nature of lichen communities [97]. Changes of microclimate in a particular area, caused in many instances by changes in the dominant vegetation, strongly influence lichen development [97]. On newly exposed substrates many lichens become well established and form thalli and fruits within two to eight years [87].

The average annual radial increments of many lichens are less than one millimeter. Crustose forms are generally the slowest growers [48, 97, 110]. The greatest amount of yearly growth of a lichen was recorded for a thallus of *Peltigera praetextata* which had an increment one year of 4.5 cm [57]. In general, species of *Peltigera* are the most rapid growers with average annual increments of 2–3 cm [57, 97, 254]. Other foliose forms have annual increments of .01–1.3 cm [48, 57, 87, 97, 113, 168, 199].

Attempts to accelerate the lichen growth rate by the application of growth-stimulating substances such as gibberellic acid and 2,4-D have been successful [31].

Despite their slow growth rates, lichens are a significant part of the vegetation in many regions of the world. In timberline forests of Alaska an acre of land may contain nearly 1.5 tons, dry weight, of *Alectoria* species [81], and some *Cladonia* species, with average annual linear growth rates of 3.4–4.1 mm [243], carpet acres of rocks and soil in the northern regions and along fog-shrouded seacoasts. *Letharia vulpina* f. *californica* blankets the trunks of fir and pine trees in the Sierra Nevada Mountains of California (U.S.A.).

The slow growth of lichens may be a reflection of many factors, such as: 1. The slow growth of their individual symbionts; 2. Their low net rates of CO_2 assimilation; 3. Their nutrient-poor substrates; 4. Their exposure to environmental conditions which allow them only brief periods for optimal metabolic activities; 5. Their frequent wetting and drying; 6. Their low rates of protein synthesis. With respect to number 4, the most important limiting factor is water. Lichen thalli lose water very quickly in dry weather, and this is accompanied by a decrease of photosynthesis, due in part to a reduction in light transmission through a dry upper cortex [83]. With terrestrial lichens photosynthesis decreases more gradually than respiration during drying [215], although Bliss and Hadley [42] found the reverse to be true for some alpine lichens. However, respiration persists, at reduced rates, even under air-dried conditions [42, 210]. Under natural conditions most lichens have only a few early morning hours following wetting by fog or dew [57] or short periods after saturation by rain or melting snow or ice when the water content of their thalli is at an optimal point for photosynthesis. Fog is the most important factor in rapid lichen development. It tends to delay drying and thus prolongs the optimum water contents for photosynthesis [57]. Light intensities during foggy periods are also at optimal levels for photosynthesis [42]. With regard to number five, when many lichens are rewetted after short periods of drought, they show a strong, often long-lasting increase in respiration [82, 154, 217]. Coupled with this, there is a strong, initial decrease of photosynthesis, which sometimes persists for days before reaching normal values if the drying period is particularly severe and prolonged [217] (Figure 47). This unfavorable photosynthetic-respiratory balance can be prolonged by several short successive drought periods and thus result in a negative food balance. With regard to number six, although this has been demonstrated only for

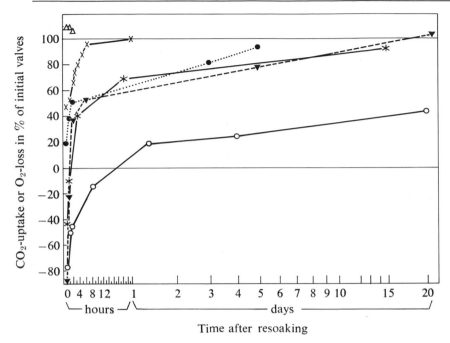

FIGURE 47. Secondary effects of 5–12 day dry periods on the photosynthesis of *Rhizocarpon geographicum* (Δ), *Lecidea soredizodes* (X), *Aspicilia lacustris* (*), *Dermatocarpon aquaticum* ($\blacktriangledown$), *Porina lectissima* ($\bullet$), and *Verrucaria elaeomelaena* (O). From Ried, 1960 [217].

Peltigera polydactyla [251, 252], it may be a general characteristic for lichens.

Culture

A major problem in experimental lichenology is the inability to culture lichens under laboratory conditions. There are two reasons for this: first, it is difficult to remove foreign organisms from a thallus without damaging the lichen symbionts, and second, the association tends to break down because of the culture conditions. Attempts to solve these difficulties have had limited success. Thallus segments can be washed with plasmolyzing agents [44] or in solutions of antiseptic compounds [23, 236, 239] to destroy epiphytes. Some of the washed thallus fragments still remain viable after these treatments, but the extent of injury, both immediate and long term effects, to the symbionts has not been determined. In some species of *Cladonia* a small percentage of young squamules dissected from the substrate and placed onto a nutrient agar remained free from contaminants [12]. After a few weeks, however, these lobes broke down into separate growths of the fungus and alga. With respect to the instability of a lichen symbiosis, a nutrient-deficient substrate can be used as a culture medium in order to prevent or, at least, to retard the breakdown of the association [24, 236, 239].

One lichen species, with a granular, crustose thallus, has been found to grow well under greenhouse conditions [67].

For short-term physiological or developmental studies, discs punched out from a thallus by means of a cork borer or similar device [236, 239] can be used. The discs of large foliose thalli can be dissected into two tissue systems, a medullary and an algal zone (see Table 2) and comparative studies can be made with these [117, 253].

In one series of developmental studies discs were cut from lichen thalli and placed onto strips of moist filter paper, arranged along the sides of large test tubes, whose lower ends were immersed in water or mineral solutions [236, 239]. The cultures were incubated at 20C and illuminated for sixteen hours a day at about 185 ft.c. Some quantitation was achieved by cutting uniform sized discs and making dry weight determinations. For discs not washed with an antiseptic solution, however, dry weights could not be made after a week or more of culture because of contamination. In a similar developmental study discs from *Cladonia* thalli formed podetia within three to five days after being placed onto moist filter paper [23, 24]. Only about 3% of the discs formed podetia. The podetia originated from hyphae directly beneath the algal layer. They forced their way through the upper surface (Figure 48) and reached an initial average height of 1.5 mm, a surprisingly rapid growth when it is considered that lichens have growth rates which average only a few millimeters a year. The podetia were of fungal origin but they were covered with fragments of the algal layer. In some species pycnidia and immature apothecia developed on the podetial tips. The factors which stimulated the formation of the podetia and reproductive structures were not clearly determined. Drying may have been involved because the discs were soaked in water for hours before being placed onto the filter paper. The greatest production of these structures occurred on discs from thalli collected during spring and fall.

Photosynthesis

The photosynthetic rates of lichens vary greatly, not only among different species but also among individuals of a single species growing in differ-

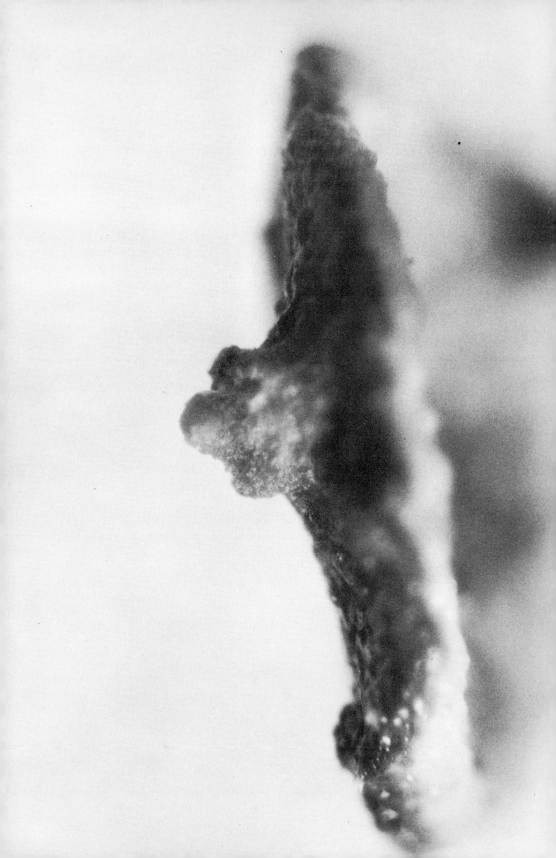

ent habitats [57, 216]. Several factors influence the rate of lichen photosynthesis, which has been measured usually by the amount of CO_2 absorbed over a certain time period by a known area or weight of thallus tissue. Perhaps the most important factor that governs the photosynthetic rates is the water content of a thallus. With many lichens, as the thallus begins to dry from a point of maximum water saturation, the rate of photosynthesis increases and reaches a peak somewhere between 65–90% of the maximum water content, below which, in the course of further water loss, the rate steadily decreases [123, 144, 192, 216, 262, 265]. The increased photosynthesis is related to the appearance during thallus shrinkage of fine air capillaries between hyphal cells of the cortex, which allow CO_2 to pass to the underlying algal cells. CO_2 is an important factor which, when it is in small supply, prevents the maximum amount of photosynthesis. Decrease of photosynthesis with further drying probably is due to factors other than the CO_2 supply, such as reduced light transmission and increased dehydration of the algal chloroplasts. The structure of a thallus (Figure 49) plays an important role in the relationship between photosynthesis and water saturation [216]. Lichens with compact thalli and thick, uninterrupted cortical layers show an increased rate only when the water content of the thallus is comparatively low. For example, the photosynthetic maximum of *Umbilicaria cylindrica* occurs at a relative water content of 65%. When cells of the compacted layers of this lichen become swollen owing to water uptake, they present a significant barrier to gas exchange. Loosely organized thalli and ones without a cortex on their lower surface, and also those with large masses of soredia—structures which resist wetting—do not hinder, to any great extent, the passage of CO_2 to the algae, even at the maximum level of saturation. Photosynthetic peaks of these lichens occur at 90% of maximum water saturation, with a small decline above this value [216]. Some large, foliose lichens have pitlike openings scattered over the undersurface of their thalli. These openings probably facilitate gas exchange. Aquatic lichens appear to have adapted to their habitat, in that maximum photosynthesis occurs even at 100% saturation [216].

Another important rate-limiting factor in lichen photosynthesis is light. Once again the water content of a thallus plays an important role. Ertl

FIGURE 48. (opposite) A thallus disc of *Cladonia coniocraea* showing a young podetium emerging through the upper layers of the thallus. (90 x) From Ahmadjian, 1963 [10].

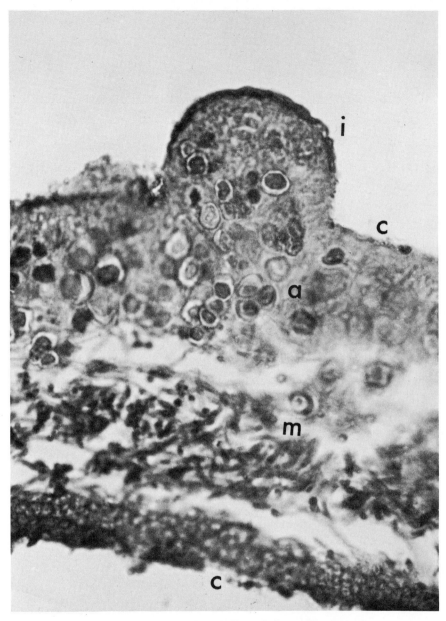

FIGURE 49. Vertical section of the thallus of *Parmelia conspersa*. c = cortex (upper and lower); a = algal layer; m = medulla, i = isidium (a small, erumpent segment of the thallus that may break away and act as an asexual propagule). (1000 x)

[83] showed that in lichens which are not pigmented the amount of light which passed through a wet cortex ranged from 55–76% of the total that fell on the thallus surface. With most pigmented lichens almost half or more of the light which fell on the thallus was absorbed or dispersed by a wet cortex. When the cortex was dry, light transmission was reduced even more—often by half—especially with the colored forms, so that in some cases little more than 20% of the light which struck the upper surface was transmitted. Light transmission through the cortex varies among different parts of a thallus. In unpigmented lichens the transmission of light becomes progressively less from the marginal lobes to the center of a thallus because of the increased thickness of the cortex in older parts. In pigmented lichens, however, there is more light transmission in the center of a thallus because of the breakdown of lichen acids and pigments in these older parts. Lichens that grow in areas exposed to high light intensities have thicker cortical and algal layers, and the reduction of light by the cortex is greater than similar individuals growing in shaded areas [83]. Also, the sun forms tend to contain more lichen acids and other pigments than shade forms [240]; this is another factor which reduces light transmission.

Studies of light transmission have been made by dissecting the different layers of a thallus and taking readings with a photocell placed behind various parts of the layers [83]. To study the amount of available light which the algal layer absorbed, a photocell was placed behind a portion of a dissected thallus composed only of the cortex and algal layers. Readings then were compared with those obtained from the cortical layer alone. By extracting the pigments from the algal layers and measuring total light absorption, Ertl [83] found that of the light available to the phycobiont about 25% was absorbed by the algal pigments—a figure slightly less than that for the foliage leaves of higher plants.

The range of light intensities at which maximum photosynthesis occurs in lichens is, at optimal temperatures (15–20C), about 400–2300 ft.c. [42, 259, 262]. Light compensation points—that is, the point at which the rates of respiration and photosynthesis are equal—lie between 15–350 ft.c. [42, 259, 262, 265]. These values, like those of optimal light intensity, vary with temperature and humidity. The amount of light needed for optimum photosynthesis is higher in the spring and summer than in the winter [262]. Photosynthetic rates of lichens vary widely in their responses to different light intensities, especially at the lower values. Some show only a slow increase in rate, while others under the same intensity have a very rapid increase. A decrease in the number of daily light hours [262] or a lowering of the light intensity [57] results in lower optimal temperatures for maximum net gain in photosynthesis, i.e., true photosynthesis. The explanation for this is that at lower temperatures respiration is inhibited more than photosynthesis [57, 261]. This is an adaptation of the lichen to climatic conditions. When the days are short, as in the fall, or the light intensities lower, as in the winter, the temperature optimum shifts and the largest possible daily photosynthetic surplus can be achieved.

A third rate-limiting factor of lichen photosynthesis is temperature. Optimal temperatures vary with different lichens, season, habitat, and light intensity. For some temperate zone lichens the optimal temperature range for photosynthesis (1600 ft.c.) is 10–20C [42, 262], and the rates are generally higher in fall and winter than in spring and summer, in some cases even at the same temperatures [262]. In general, however, the optimal temperatures for maximum photosynthesis are lower in winter (average of 14.1C) than in spring and summer (average of 18.5C) [262]. True photosynthesis—that is, the respiratory rate of the lichens as measured in darkness, plus the apparent or net photosynthetic rate—increases to a certain degree at lower temperatures [262]. Net photosynthesis is measured without regard for respiration which is occurring at the same time. The increased photosynthetic efficiency, over a twenty-four hour period, in winter may be related to a lowered respiration rate with no similar decrease in photosynthesis or to a finding that lichens have one-half to one-third more chlorophyll in the winter than summer [299]. This may be related to an increase in the number of algal cells in a given area of thallus during the winter.

Lichens which grow in cold areas of the world have temperature optima of under 10C for net photosynthesis (1000 ft.c.), and even below 0C the amount of CO_2 absorption and fixation is considerable [156, 157, 160]. For example, *Letharia vulpina* at a thallus temperature of −5C and in spite of ice formation in its medulla, still fixed half of the CO_2 that it normally would have under optimal conditions (Figure 50). That this phenomenon was an adaptation to a particular environment was illustrated by a comparison with the photosynthetic rates of tropical forms which first reached optimum levels at temperatures above 20C. Some lichen species had a positive CO_2 balance, due to real photosynthesis, at thallus temperatures down to −24C [156, 157] and even tropical forms with optimal values above 20C still maintained a positive CO_2 balance at a temperature of —3C. Another adaptation which cold-area lichens exhibit is their ability to resume within a brief period of time maximum rates of photosynthesis after long periods of freezing. In one experiment [156] *Cladonia alcicornis* could still photosynthesize after a freezing period of about two

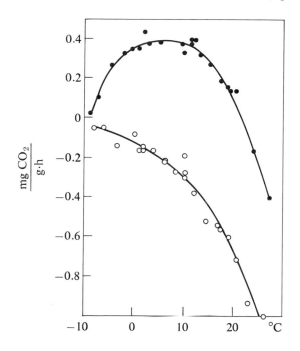

FIGURE 50. CO_2-gas exchange of *Letharia vulpina* in light (10,000 lux) (dots) and in dark (circles), as a function of temperature. Abscissus = thallus temperature; ordinate = uptake or loss of CO_2. From "Der CO_2-Gaswechsel von Flechten bei tiefen Temperaturen," O. L. Lange, *Planta*, Bd 64, S. 1–19. (Berlin, Heidelberg, New York: Springer, 1965).

years at —15C in darkness. Moist lichens are very sensitive to heat. Temperatures of 32–40C can seriously affect their photosynthesis. In a dried condition, however, heat resistance is increased considerably [158].

The photosynthetic rates of lichens generally are much lower than those of the leaves of higher plants. However, a given fresh weight or area of lichen tissue would contain fewer photosynthetic units than a comparable weight or area of a leaf. The rates of CO_2 absorption of six terrestrial lichens in air and under favorable conditions for photosynthesis ranged from 0.34–3.1 mg/CO_2/ 50 cm² of thallus area/ hour [215]. Bliss and Hadley [42] reported optimal rates of 0.30–0.38 mg/CO_2/ g dry wt/hr for three alpine lichens. A possible reason for the low photosynthetic rates of lichens, which may be related to their having fewer photosynthetic cells for a given area of thallus, is the finding that some lichens have smaller amounts of chlorophyll than leaves [299]. Lichens examined during the winter had one-fourth to one-tenth as much chlorophyll as leaves.

Crustose lichens show greater individual variation of photosynthesis than foliose forms. This is because of the more irregular thicknesses of crustose thalli [215]. Photosynthetic rates of the two lichen types, however, occupy the same range of maximum and minimum values. In contrast, the average respiration rates of crustose lichens are lower than those of foliose types, and the variability which is found in the respiration rates of crustose lichens is greater than photosynthesis, since an algal layer would show smaller size differences than a thallus as a whole [215]. One of the problems in studying the metabolic activities of lichens is the difficulty in obtaining uniform samples. Different parts of even a single thallus may vary in width, color, age, and number of algal cells, thus making it difficult to compare the results of investigations. The different methods which have been used to test and measure metabolic rates also have added to the confusion.

Respiration

The following endogenous respiration rates have been recorded for lichens and their separate symbionts [12]. For nine *Trebouxia* phycobionts of temperate and antarctic lichens, the endogenous Q_{o2} values at 35C ranged from 0.2–5.8 (μl O_2/hr/mg dry wt). A *Coccomyxa* phycobiont had values of 9–12 under the same conditions. For numerous mycobionts, the endogenous Q_{o2} values at 35C ranged from 0.3–7.3. There were no significant differences among tropical, temperate, and antarctic forms. For six temperate-zone lichens, with *Trebouxia* as phycobionts, endogenous Q_{o2} values at 35C ranged from 0.5–1.6.

Respiration of terrestrial lichens does not decrease at maximum water saturation, but below a certain level of water content, usually 80% of the maximum value, a rapid decrease accompanies drying of the thallus [215, 216]. The decline in respiration occurs more rapidly than photosynthesis, but a small amount of respiration usually persists, unlike photosynthesis, even under air-dried conditions when a thallus may have a water content as low as 6.7% of maximum with *Peltigera* species [259] and 0.4% with *Teloschistes flavicans* [69]. A decrease in the respiration of an aquatic lichen began at a very low relative water content (40%), lower than the point (70%) below which its rate of photosynthesis began to decrease [216].

Respiration rates of lichens do not show the same seasonal variation as photosynthesis, and even among lichens of different climatic areas the respiratory differences are small. In one experiment designed to ascertain whether at low temperatures arctic lichens had higher rates of respiration than tropical forms [231], the results from nineteen arctic and ten tropical species in general showed no significant differences. Optimal temperatures for respiration ranged from 20–30C in both groups, and the lower temperatures slowed the respiration rates of arctic species as much as those of the tropical forms. Unfortunately, it was not possible to obtain the same species of lichens from both regions, and since there was a great variability of respiration rates—these were measured in terms of O_2 consumption— among the different species in each area, it was difficult to make any but the most general comparisons. Species of *Peltigera* and *Sticta* had the highest rates in both groups, and the arctic forms of these species at 10C respired as high as the tropical forms at 20C, giving some indication of cold adaptation.

One factor which must be considered in a study of this type is the microclimate. The temperatures of thalli and substrates during an arctic or antarctic summer are usually higher than those of the air a few feet above them. This is due to the warming effect of the sun. In Antarctica during late summer dark rocks may have surface temperatures which exceed 32C, while the air temperature a few feet above them does not exceed 8C [219]. Since the metabolism of the cold region lichens is adapted to low temperatures [157], a fair, warm day would be detrimental to them.

Respiration still persists at low temperatures, down to −26C in several arctic lichens [232], but, like photosynthesis, it is less resistant to higher temperatures (35–45C), except when the lichen is in a dried condition [144]. Between 0C or lower, up to 35C, the respiration rates rise steadily with increased temperatures in winter as well as in summer [259, 262].

The respiratory quotients (R.Q.), or the ratio of CO_2 produced to O_2 taken up (CO_2/O_2), of lichens range from 0.73–0.85, and down to 0.60 in several instances [117, 144]. R.Q. values are used to help determine the type of nutrients which are metabolized by an organism. For example, a ratio of one, or approximately one, indicates a sugar or carbohydrate substrate, because during the complete oxidation of a hexose sugar one molecule of CO_2 is produced for every molecule of oxygen used. R.Q. values of less than one indicate metabolism of fats and proteins where the amount of oxygen needed for combustion is greater than the CO_2 released. Whether the low R.Q. values of the endogenous respiration of lichens—that is, the utilization of materials within the cells rather than from an external source —are true indicators of their respiratory substrates is not known. There is a possibility that the low values reflect an accumulation of organic acids, the formation of which is accompanied by considerable oxygen uptake and little CO_2 evolution. A gradual rise from an R.Q. of 0.87 to 1.0 was noted for a *Parmelia physodes* specimen which was kept moist for several days following an eighteen-day dry period. The rise was attributed to the formation and respiration of sugars under moist conditions and the respiration at the beginning of the moist period of fats, which were observed in the algal cells during the dry period [82]. Algae tend to form and accumulate fats during periods of nitrogen deficiency or other adverse growth conditions [88]. In *Peltigera polydactyla* a rise of the R.Q. to 1.25 was noted after sugar was added to its medium [117]. This might be explained by periods of anaerobic conditions within the thallus [211].

The effects of different substrates on respiration have been studied with *Peltigera polydactyla* and *Cladonia rangiferina*. In the first, lichen discs of the thallus were used, and in the second, the thallus tissue was homogenized. With *Peltigera* separate additions of ammonia, asparagine, glucose, sucrose, and phosphate increased respiration rates [117, 251, 252, 253]. With *Cladonia* glutamate and a protein mixture were respired more rapidly than acetate and lactate, while glycerol and glucose suppressed slightly the respiration rate [227]. With *Peltigera* sodium fluoride stimulated the rate of oxygen uptake [117], probably by inhibiting the process of oxidative phosphorylation. Usnic acid, one of the most common of lichen substances, has a similar effect on animal tissues [142, 260], but its effect on lichens is not known.

Water Relations

There have been many investigations of the water relations of lichens, and the information obtained has contributed greatly to our understanding of the distribution of these plants. The existence of lichens in some of the driest parts of the world and their luxuriant development on fog-shrouded mountains and coasts is better understood from a knowledge of how, when, and in what form they absorb and lose water.

The uptake of water by lichens is almost entirely a physical process much like the absorption of moisture by gelatine or agar [68, 69, 136, 192, 259, 265, 266]. Lichens do not actively absorb water from their substrates, they do not have conductive tissues, and they do not have physiological control over their water contents. The amount of water within a thallus fluctuates markedly during a twenty-four hour period, according to the atmospheric conditions. Water can be taken up in liquid form either from rain, fog, or dew, and from vapor. Absorption of water takes place over the whole thallus surface, both upper and lower sides, and with gelatinous lichens the slimy cellular sheaths of the blue-green phycobionts increase their absorption capabilities.

Under natural conditions lichens frequently are dry, with water contents that range from 2–10% of their dry weights [154, 192]. When a dry, brittle thallus is submerged in water, it becomes soft and pliable within a few seconds. In five seconds air-dried lichens can take up half of the maximum amount of water they can hold, and after thirty seconds the plants are close to being fully saturated [265]. Other lichens take longer to become completely saturated, up to ninety minutes [136, 150, 215], with water contents that go as high as 365% of dry weight in *Umbilicaria mammulata* [230] and much higher in gelatinous lichens [266]. The variation in saturation time depends on how thick a thallus is and the amount of crystals which encrust the fungal hyphae [150, 215]. In general, most of the water absorption occurs in the first few minutes. This rapid uptake of water by lichens is due to a system of air-filled spaces which appear between the cortical hyphae during dry conditions. It is into these spaces that the water first enters and then rapidly penetrates to the interior layers [265]. Since these open areas are also present in dead lichens, the amount and speed of water uptake is similar to that of living forms [29, 259]. Water is held not only in extracellular capillaries but also in the thick hyphal walls of the fungus which expand and become saturated within a few minutes after wetting [265]. As might be expected, the absorbed water is lost very rapidly under drying conditions. A saturated thallus after a thirty-minute exposure to the sun becomes brittle, and after one hour it is fully dried [265]. In shaded conditions the water loss takes about twice as long. From an ecological standpoint, this rapid loss of water by a thallus growing on an exposed, sunny substrate is important because it allows the lichen to survive high temperatures, which it can do only in a dried condition [154]. Moreover, the rapid drying is essential in that the dry cortex of a thallus reduces the light intensity which reaches the algal cells. High light intensities can damage algal cells, especially when they are in moist conditions. From a physiological viewpoint, however, the water loss is disadvantageous because the rapid drying reduces or stops photosynthesis entirely, usually below 30% water content [215, 216, 259], while respiration still continues at low rates even under air-dried conditions. In many areas lichens have only a few hours in the morning, after dewfall or after a rainstorm, during which maximum or near-maximum photosynthesis occurs. The amount of surplus food, if any, which is gained during this short time is small. If the drying were delayed by means of high humidity, fog, or because the lichen faced west, then the time for optimal photosynthesis would be prolonged, allowing for a greater photosynthetic surplus [57]. Fog appears to be the most important factor in the rapid development of lichens, especially for those growing on a substrate which does not retain much water. The luxuriant lichen growth in mountains, northern regions, and coastal areas is not dependent as much on the quantity and frequency of rain as on the frequency and thickness of fog [265]. In the arid, coastal regions of Peru and Chile there is no rainfall as such, but in the winter these areas frequently are covered with fog. This type of moisture does not provide sufficient water to support higher plants, but it does result in abundant lichen growth [71]. The abundance of lichens, especially in coastal areas, on exposures which face west is due probably to the few extra hours, after sunrise, during which these forms can maintain the high water contents caused by nightly fogs.

During rainless periods, lichens behave as hygrometers, and their water contents fluctuate with the air humidity [121, 230, 265]. Absorption of water vapor is a slow process compared to the uptake of liquid water, and a constant equilibrium value is reached only after days or weeks [57, 68, 69, 136, 150, 208, 215, 259, 265]. Even under conditions of 95% relative humidity, after weeks water contents are reached which are only 30–50% of the maximum value [57, 121, 215, 265] (Figure 51). Under natural conditions high relative humidities, which result only in small increases of water in a thallus, are actually harmful to lichens. The small increase will stimulate respiration, but the water content still remains below the minimum level required for photosynthesis or causes only a reduced photosynthetic activity, below that of respiration [265]. Some desert lichens are able to undergo considerable photosynthesis with only water vapor [159]. Some granular, crustose lichens, such as species of *Calcium* and *Lepraria*, are unwettable. They are not able to take up liquid water even if they are kept submerged for hours. Moreover, certain of these lichens grow in habitats like the undersurface of overhanging rocks where rain does not reach them. These lichens depend on air moisture as their only available water supply. They have adapted to this lack of liquid water by being able to absorb water vapor very quickly [57] and lose it more slowly than other wettable lichens. Since these lichens cannot be weighed because they are so closely attached to a substrate, their photosynthetic rates are

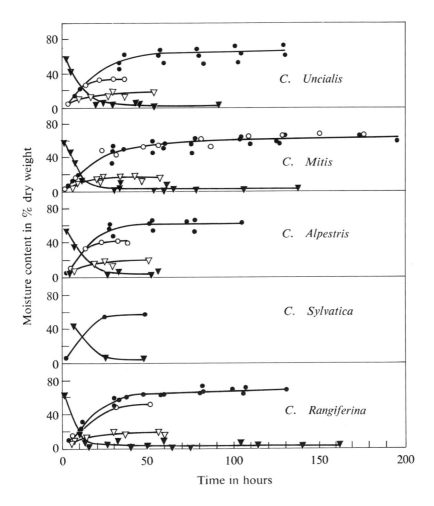

FIGURE 51. Rates of absorption and loss of water by *Cladonia* under different conditions of relative humidity. Dots represent values obtained at near 100% r.h., open triangles those at 75% r.h., and solid triangles, those at 12% r.h. Circles represent values obtained at 100% r.h. but using thalli which had first been killed by oven drying at 105C for 12 hours. From Heatwole, 1966 [121].

used as indicators of water saturation [57]. When a lichen of this type was placed in a saturated atmosphere (100% relative humidity), the maximum photosynthetic rate was achieved after six to eight hours [57].

There are no specific water storage areas within a thallus. Some lichens, such as *Cladonia*, retain large amounts of water in their upright, hollow podetia and the central cord of an *Usnea* filament can store one-third of the total water content of the lichen. Water can be retained for brief periods in thick medullary layers, pits and channels in a thallus, between numerous rhizinae, and isidia [206]. The dead algal and fungal cells within a thallus also may serve in this capacity [250]. Some desert and antarctic lichens have adapted to their environments by the formation of thick, compact upper cortical layers and sometimes, in addition, different types of amorphous layers which cover the thallus. These structures retard evaporation [79, 84, 103, 288].

Substrate

The substrates to which lichens are attached may play important roles, apart from support, in their nutrition and water relations. Lichens can absorb and accumulate a wide variety of materials from their substrates including considerable amounts of minerals [172, 173, 255]. Lichens that grow on silicic and ultrabasic rocks have been found to contain large amounts of trace elements, particularly zinc, which in some thalli was found in concentrations of up to 13,000 p.p.m. and lead, found in concentrations as high as 3000 p.p.m. The amounts of gallium, yttrium, and tin were surprisingly high. Other elements which were present within thalli were boron, cadmium, chromium, cobalt, copper, iron, manganese, molybdenum, nickel, silver, zinc, and zirconium. Lichens that grow on rocks which contain unusual amounts of a mineral generally show a correspondingly high content of the element [172]. High concentrations of elements in the uranium-radium, actinouranium, and thorium orders have been discovered in lichens, a finding which may or perhaps already has led to a novel way of prospecting for these minerals—namely, by scanning lichen collections with a Geiger counter [226]. Probably many lichens take up essential metallic elements from their rock substrates by means of acids which are excreted by hyphae of the fungal components [228]. Lichen acids are effective chelating agents [226]—that is they can bind metal atoms between atoms of their own molecules. Chelation is an important factor in the chemical weathering or slow disintegration of rocks and formation of soil by lichens, and the ability of an acid to dissolve a particular type of rock and not another may be a determining factor in the distribution of rock colonizing lichens. Lichens can cause physical weathering of rock surfaces. Many thalli are pressed closely against their substrates. Some are immersed in the substratum and others form close contacts by means of rhizinae (Figure 52) which penetrate small chinks or cracks in rocks or barks of trees. As the thalli and rhizinae swell and shrink because of daily

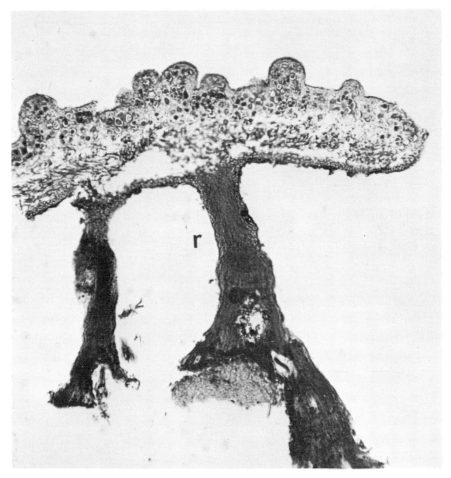

FIGURE. 52. Vertical section of a *Parmelia conspersa* thallus showing rhizinae (r).   (100 x)

fluctuations in their water contents, and as growth occurs, regardless of how small, pressures are introduced which cause particles of the substrate to become detached [100, 101]. These fragments eventually become embedded in the thallus where they are decomposed further by lichen acids. Lichens are highly efficient accumulators of radioactive fallout [106]. Recent studies have traced the reason for the high levels of cesium-137 and strontium-90 found in Alaskan Eskimos and Scandinavian Lapplanders from the caribou and reindeer on which these people feed, back to the lichens which form a principal part of the diet of these animals [195, 222, 293]. High concentrations of the naturally occurring radioisotopes lead-210 and polonium-210 in Alaskan Eskimos followed a similar pattern [34].

The supposed role of lichens in soil formation seems exaggerated. Although a limited action by lichens on their substrates has been demonstrated, it seems unlikely that they would make any significant contribution to forming soil, except in areas where some "reindeer lichens," which form extensive mats, decay and form a type of humus.

Lichens can absorb organic compounds from their substrates, thereby supplementing what they synthesize by photosynthesis. Obviously, the amount of materials obtained in this manner is not large, since this would tend to disrupt the balanced growth of the symbionts and cause a breakdown of the association. Organic nitrogen compounds were shown to be present in the water which passed over *Peltigera polydactyla,* a woodland lichen which grows on soil and mosses [252]. Moreover, laboratory studies using thallus discs have revealed that this lichen, as well as other tested species, can absorb from solution many substances, including sugars, amino acids, ammonia, nitrates, and phosphate [117, 251–254, 257]. These materials were utilized at a slow rate and accumulated in the thallus during certain periods of the year when they were present in abundance. The large populations of microorganisms, such as bacteria, actinomycetes, and fungi, which are present on substrates colonized by lichens, probably play a role in making assimilable compounds available to lichens by a chemical action either on the substrate or on complex organic compounds which accumulate from the death of older parts of thalli and from dust and debris which are trapped by many thalli. The presence of extracellular enzymes in lichens suggests that lichens themselves are active also in making assimilable compounds available from their substrates. Some of the more common lichen enzymes, which are similar to those of free-living, saprophytic fungi, are amylase, asparaginase, catalase, cellulase, lichenase, sucrase, urease, and zymase [181].

Absorption and Metabolism

The absorption and utilization of various substances by lichens can be studied by a technique which involves cutting out uniform-sized discs from a thallus and floating them on solutions which contain the compounds to be tested. Large thalli can be dissected into two parts, one which contains the cortical and algal layers and another composed of the medulla (see Table 2). Both parts then can be tested separately. Most of the studies on absorption and metabolism have been conducted with *Peltigera poly-dactyla*, which has *Nostoc* as a phycobiont [117, 251–254, 257].

The uptake of materials in solution by *Peltigera* takes place rapidly by means of an active transport. Absorption rates are inhibited by sodium fluoride and silver nitrate, and increased respiration accompanies absorption. In mixed equimolar solutions glucose is absorbed preferentially to fructose and sucrose, and there is evidence for a surface enzyme which breaks down sucrose to glucose and fructose. As might be expected, the thallus layer composed of the algal zone is more active in sugar absorption than the medulla. An experiment which utilized labeled glucose revealed that half of all the glucose absorbed within twenty-four hours by *Peltigera* discs was converted into the sugar alcohol mannitol, 20% was converted to a glucose polysaccharide, 20% was released as carbon dioxide, 5% was converted to a galactose-mannitol glycoside, and the rest to unknown substances. No free glucose was found in the extracts of the discs which indicated a rapid conversion into other substances. A comparative study between the two dissected thallus layers showed that both sections converted glucose to mannitol, but only the algal-cortex layer synthesized the glycoside and polysaccharide from the absorbed glucose. In another study which investigated the incorporation of $C^{14}O_2$ into discs of *Peltigera aphthosa*, which has *Coccomyxa* as a phycobiont, mannitol was not one of the compounds found in extracts of the discs. Rather, large amounts of labeled sucrose were present, along with glucose and fructose, organic acids, and amino acids [38].

Mannitol is abundant in many lichens [167, 205], but its role in the carbon metabolism of these organisms has not been established. It may be a storage compound which, along with various glycosides, is translocated from the algal zone to the medulla where it accumulates and forms a food reserve [254, 257]. Other sugar alcohols that are formed by lichens are arabitol, which is almost as widespread in occurrence as mannitol, and volemitol. Sugar alcohols may constitute up to 4.9% of the dry weight of a lichen [205] and are more abundant in a thallus than the simple sugars such as fructose, galactose, glucose, mannose, sucrose, and treholose, which also may be present. Glycosides are also common in lichens. A galactose-arabitol glycoside (umbilicin) and a galactose-mannitol glycoside (peltigeroside) have been found in widely different genera [166, 204, 205]. Lichen polysaccharides, which consist of varying amounts of galactose, glucose, and mannose, include lichenin, isolichenin, pustulan, and others as yet unnamed [28, 80, 198, 298]. In many instances, it is not known whether these compounds are products or constituents of the fungal or algal symbionts.

There is little information on the amounts and types of nitrogen compounds which are available to a lichen in its natural habitat [247]. Nitrogen fixation occurs in lichens with species of *Nostoc* as phycobiont [45, 236], but whether the nitrogen obtained is sufficient to meet their needs is not known. *Peltigera* discs can absorb a variety of nitrogenous substances from solution [251, 252]. The uptake of asparagine by the lichen was particularly rapid when compared to aspartic acid, glutamic acid, and glutamine. During absorption of these compounds ammonia was released into the medium. Asparagine appeared to enter the lichen as a complete molecule and accumulated in the thallus. Its rate of assimilation was slow compared to its rapid absorption. Half of the absorbed asparagine still remained in the discs seventy-two hours after an absorption period, indicating a slow incorporation into protein. Not only was there a slow rate of protein synthesis by *Peltigera* discs but the rates of protein breakdown were slow when compared to other plants. Discs kept in the dark on distilled water for seven days showed only a 5–10% breakdown of protein [251, 254]. If the slow synthesis and degradation of proteins and perhaps carbohydrates as well [257] are common characteristics of lichens, they would certainly be important adaptations to the barren habitats which these organisms occupy [252].

Resistance to Environmental Extremes

Most lichens are very resistant to extremes of temperature and drying. Unfortunately, the methods which have been used to determine such resistance all show certain limitations. One complication is that the partners may differ in their susceptibility to certain conditions. For example, in some lichens one partner can withstand many weeks of drying while the other is damaged within a few weeks [154]. Lichen viability is difficult to determine. The fact that after a test period a dry thallus turns green when wetted is not an indication that the lichen is alive. Attempts can be made to culture the components, but this does not show the extent of damage which may have occurred. Microscopic examinations of thalli are useful only if the test conditions have caused visible cell damage. Respiration rates can be used to measure vitality, but there still remains an uncertainty whether the activity is a result of both components or only one. Nonetheless, the tests most commonly employed have measured rates of gaseous exchange.

Lichens are very resistant to low temperatures. Specimens frozen in liquid oxygen at −183C for eighteen hours still respired when thawed and kept at a warmer temperature [232]. A specimen of *Xanthoria parietina* has been reported to have withstood a temperature close to absolute zero (−273C)—a characteristic which it shared with some mosses, algae, and insects [35, 36, 37]—and moreover, to have retained vitality after six years in a vacuum. Since lichens cannot be grown in a laboratory and their natural growth rates are so slow, it is difficult to determine what the aftereffects may be of a particular treatment. Becquerel, the investigator who conducted these experiments, speculated on the interesting possibility of lichens and other organisms still being viable after being buried for thousands of years under antarctic ice.

The ability to withstand high temperatures varies according to the ecological habitat. Lange [154] found that lichens from cool, moist areas were less resistant than those from hot, dry locations. *Usnea* and *Alectoria* were particularly sensitive genera. A thirty-minute exposure of air-dried specimens to 70C reduced by half their normal respiration rates. *Umbilicaria* was an example of a resistant genus whose rate of respiration was halved only at temperatures close to 100C. When lichens are moist, their resistance limits drop by 40–50C. The resistance of lichens in a dried condition to heat is understandable when it is considered that on a hot summer's day exposed lichen thalli may reach temperatures of 50–70C, possibly higher [154, 155].

Lichens also can withstand dry periods for considerable lengths of time, far longer than what they normally encounter in their natural habitats. Even the least resistant lichens can withstand up to sixteen weeks of constant drying either under dry air conditions or over a dehydrating agent such as phosphorus pentoxide. More resistant forms survive for over one year without detectable signs of damage [154].

Few lichens can survive the environment of industrialized areas [147,

269].   A notable exception is *Lecanora conizaeoides* which somehow has adapted to life near large cities and towns. Air pollution appears to be the primary cause for the absence of lichens near urban areas with the extreme dryness of these regions being a secondary factor. Sulfur dioxide is the most toxic component of polluted air for lichens and its absorption by lichen thalli causes degradation of chlorophyll a [213].

6 ❧ Lichen Chemistry

Researchers have been interested for years in lichen substances, not only because of their simple structural configurations, which are well suited for biosynthetic studies, but also because of their biological activities. Many of the one hundred or more lichen substances have antimicrobial properties. The variety of lichen compounds has been described in detail by Asahina and Shibata [27], Shibata [244, 245] and Hale [114].

Most lichen products are aromatic compounds of which the two most common and characteristic groups (in the sense that with one known exception they are produced only by lichens) are depsides and depsidones (Figure 53). A compound of either type is formed by two or three simple phenylcarboxylic acids, mainly orsellinic or beta-orsellinic acids, held together by an ester linkage. In a depsidone there is an additional oxygen bridge as a result of a phenol coupling or dehydrogenation of the depside nucleus [65, 178, 244, 290]. These compounds contain aliphatic side chains composed of uneven numbers of carbon atoms. About thirty types of depsides and fifteen depsidones have been identified from lichens [114]. Although nonlichenized fungi produce monocyclic phenolic compounds similar to those which form depsides [135], only one free-living fungus, *Aspergillus nidulans*, has been reported to produce the same type of diphenyl compounds found in lichens [72]. Other aromatic compounds which lichens produce are quinones, pulvic acid derivatives, xanthone de-

113

rivatives, and dibenzofuran derivatives. Aliphatic and alicyclic lichen substances include monobasic, dibasic, and tribasic acids, triterpenoids, and polyhydric alcohols.

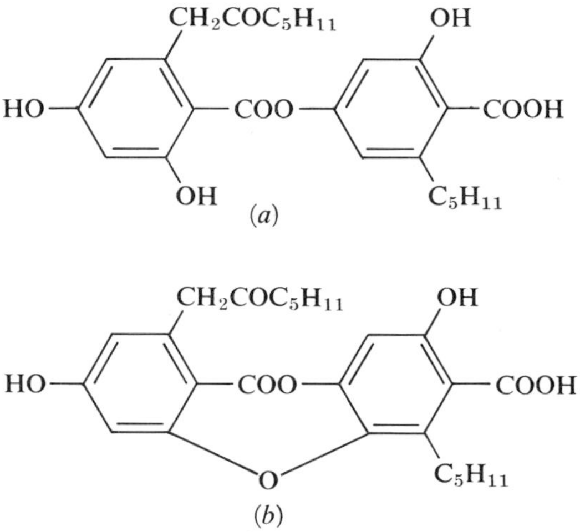

FIGURE 53. (a) Olivetoric acid, a depside; (b) Physodic acid, a depsidone. From C. F. Culberson, *Science*, 143 (January 17, 1964), 255–56. Copyright 1964 by the American Association for the Advancement of Science.

Lichen substances are found commonly as granules or crystals on the outer surfaces of hyphae within a thallus, usually in the cortex or medulla. Several functions have been attributed to these extracellular products. They may play a role in protecting the slow growing thalli from decomposition by bacteria and molds, damage by insects, or overgrowth by mosses and hepatics. There is some evidence which supports this [116, 122], but in view of the often luxuriant populations of microorganisms and insects which inhabit thalli, this proposed role seems exaggerated. Pigments which are localized usually in the upper cortex and are very abundant in sunexposed lichens serve a protective function for the alga by absorbing much of the light that falls on a thallus [212]. Because of the low light intensities that are available to the alga in a thallus, Rao and LeBlanc [212] have proposed that fluorescent lichen compounds such as atranorin serve as accessory light absorbers in the thallus. The fluorescence spectrum of atranorin coincided with the absorption spectrum of chlorophyll in the blue region. They hypothesized that these compounds help the alga to make maximum use of the low light intensities and also the light of smaller wavelengths to which they are exposed. Lichen acids are effective chelating agents and may be a means by which essential metallic elements are obtained from rock surfaces [226, 228]. Some of these compounds may increase cell permeability of the algal symbiont [90], but there is little direct experimental evidence which supports this possibility.

Biosynthetic studies have been made by shaking the lichen in a solution of water and the radioactive precursor [186] and by spraying the tracer solution onto the lichen thallus [300]. Mosbach [186–189] found that gyrophoric acid (depside) was formed by an acetate-malonate pathway and he proposed that vulpinic acid was formed by a polyporic acid type of compound (shikimic acid pathway). Lecanoric acid and atranorin (both depsides) were shown to be formed from acetate and the functional groups in atranorin and chloroatranorin (i.e., CH_3 and CHO) were formed separately from formate [300, 301]. The incorporation of formate (or C_1 unit) occurred prior to the completion of the aromatic ring of orsellinic acid. Shibata has classified the known lichen substances by means of their biosynthetic pathways [245a].

Taxonomists are interested in lichen substances because they recognize that these compounds, with certain notable exceptions, are constant and characteristic features of particular lichens and therefore are valuable identification tools. However, the use of these compounds in lichen taxonomy is not accepted universally, and the relationship of lichen chemistry and taxonomy is still a controversial issue [70, 114, 120, 272]. Lichenologists who are accustomed to delimiting species on the basis of morphological differences find it difficult to accept new species which are based largely on chemical differences. For example, one strain of *Thamnolia vermicularis* contains thamnolic acid while another strain, morphologically identical to the first, contains baeomycic and squamatic acids and has been named *Thamnolia subuliformis*. Frequently, these chemical species have different geographical and even ecological distributions. *T. subuliformis* has a more northerly distribution than *T. vermicularis*, and *Cladonia submitis*, a chemical variant of *Cladonia mitis*, occurs in the southeastern part of the United States while its related form is found in the northern parts of North America. *Parmeliopsis ambigua* and *Parmeliopsis hyperopta* are morphologically identical, but the former contains usnic acid and grows farther up the tree bases than *P. hyperopta*, which contains atranorin. It can be postulated that the mycobionts which form these lichens, although morphologically identical, are of different physiological strains. Still another possibility is that the same fungus forms lichenized associations with different types of algae. If the algal symbiont is necessary for the final synthesis and characterization of lichen compounds, then the differences in the chemical substances may be a result of different algal components. There is evidence to show that specimens of the same lichen species collected from different localities do have algal strains which differ in physiological and morphological traits (see Chapter 4, p. 79). A striking example of one fungus that forms lichenized associations with widely different algae is found in *Lobaria pulmonaria* and *Lobaria retigera*. These two lichens also differ in the nature of their chemical substances [26]. The thalli of both lichens are morphologically identical, except that *L. pulmonaria* (stictic or norstictic acids), a temperate form, has *Coccomyxa* as its phycobiont, and *L. retigera* (thelephoric acid), a tropical form, has *Nostoc* as its algal symbiont. *L. subretigera*, however, has a blue-green phycobiont and the same metabolites as *L. pulmonaria*, which indicates that a difference in algal components does not influence the type of chemical substances in a lichen. Perhaps it is most reasonable to assume that *L. pulmonaria* and *L. retigera* are metabolically different fungi [245a]. Whether or not chemically distinct strains of a lichen deserve taxonomic recognition is debatable. Asahina, on the basis of microchemical studies, proposed to separate the *Cladonia chlorophaea* group into four species according to differences in their chemical compounds; that is, *C. chlorophaea* (fumarprotocetraric acid), *C. grayi* (grayanic acid), *C. cryptochlorophaea* (cryptochlorophaeic acid), and *C. merochlorophaea* (merochlorophaeic acid). Lamb would designate the last three species only as chemical strains of *C. chlorophaea* [246].

Chemical substances undoubtedly will play an increased role in lichen taxonomy. Fortunately, the techniques for isolation and identification of these compounds are simple and can be performed routinely [27, 114, 132, 245, 289]. The possible use in lichen taxonomy of amino acid patterns has been proposed [211a].

Considerable information exists on the antibiotic activities of lichen substances [25, 51, 52, 54, 55, 273, 284]. Many lichen acids are active against bacteria, mainly gram-positive forms, and free-living molds. Lichen extracts and acids have inhibited the activity of the tobacco mosaic virus [92, 191] and some bacteriophages [115]. They also have inhibited the seed germination and development of various plants [53, 91, 177, 193]. Usnic acid, a compound which is found in the thalli of numerous lichens, has received much attention in recent years [25, 59, 161, 267, 285, 286, 287]. This substance has a broad antibiotic spectrum and is the basis of commercial drugs in Finland ("Usno"), Germany ("Usniplant"), and Russia ("Binan"). A mixture of usnic acid and evernic acids extracted from species of *Evernia* is yet another product called "Evosin" [148]. The most effective use of these drugs is for the treatment of external wounds and infections. The antibiotic action of usnic acid lies in its ability to inhibit the oxidative-phosphorylation cycle [142], an action similar to that of dinitrophenol. The reported effective concentrations for such inhibitions and for antibiotic activity are within the same range, i.e., 2 μg/ml and 1.3–2.6 μg/ml, respectively. At a concentration of 10 μg/ml usnic acid has been shown to inhibit the dispersion of DNA in the sperm nucleus of fertilized *Arbacia* eggs. In the presence of $CoCl_2$ (.001–.002M), the sodium salt of usnic acid (1–10 μg/ml) inhibited DNA-ase activity [175]. Usnic acid also has been reported to cause human allergy [180].

Metabolites produced by lichen fungi in culture are also active against sarcomas (Abbott Laboratories, personal communication). Perhaps these compounds have a similar role of controlling or slowing the growth of the algal partner in the lichen symbiosis.

Pharmacological studies have been conducted with several lichen substances. Cetrarin was found to accelerate peristalsis in mammals and increase blood pressure and bile secretion [284]. Usnic acid and its sodium salt have been reported to relax smooth muscle [284], accelerate the rate of respiration in mammals [260], and when tested on the crop and gizzard of earthworms, at concentrations of .001–.009 μg/ml, to have activities similar to adrenaline [118]. Lichesteric acid was found to greatly promote adsorption [284]. Lethal doses for some of these substances were as follows: 75 mg/kg for vulpinic acid in the case of a cat; for usnic acid, the lethal dose for a mouse was 0.7 g/kg subcutaneously and 0.025 g/kg intravenously; for lichesteric acid, 0.1 g/kg injected intravenously into a mouse [284].

Although much work has been done on some compounds and several hundred crude lichen extracts have been tested for biological activities, there has not been made, in this respect, any large scale systematic survey of these plants. One of the limitations of such an undertaking lies in the size and abundance of thallus material from which crystalline substances can be obtained. It is difficult and often impossible to collect many lichens in sufficient quantities. This problem could be eliminated if one could induce the fungal partners alone, in axenic culture, to synthesize the same substances which they do while in the lichenized associations.

At the present time, the primary economic importance of lichens is as a fodder for reindeer and caribou herds of the arctic regions [171, 242]. Contrary to popular belief, there are not specific types of "reindeer lichens" on which these animals selectively feed, although certain forms of these plants are so prevalent in some areas that the reindeer naturally feed mostly on them. Species of a dozen or more lichen genera are utilized as food, and in the fall and winter months these plants make up a considerable part of the reindeers' diet. The nutritive value of lichen fodder is due largely to the carbohydrates lichenin and isolichenin. Proteins and fats are present, but in much lesser amounts. Vitamins such as ascorbic acid, folic acid, niacin, riboflavin, and thiamine are present [109, 151, 249] as well as ergosterol and traces of vitamin D [18, 43, 56].

Lichens have served as a source of food for humans, but only during times of starvation. Several factors prevent their general use. The bitter substances within many thalli, although nonpoisonous, irritate and inflame the digestive tract of humans. Moreover, these substances are not removed easily from the thalli. The plants are also tasteless and their slow growth rates preclude successful cultivation. ✓

Appendix

‿‿

Recommended Media for the Culture of Lichen Symbionts

A. ALGAL SYMBIONT*

Bold's Mineral Medium:†

Part I. Six stock solutions, each one 400 ml in volume, are prepared. Each solution contains one of the following salts in the quantities listed:

$$NaNO_3 \quad \ldots\ldots\ldots\ldots\ldots 10.0\,g$$
$$CaCl_2 \quad \ldots\ldots\ldots\ldots\ldots\ldots 1.0\,g$$
$$MgSO_4 \cdot 7H_2O \quad \ldots\ldots\ldots 3.0\,g$$
$$K_2HPO_4 \quad \ldots\ldots\ldots\ldots 3.0\,g$$
$$KH_2PO_4 \quad \ldots\ldots\ldots\ldots 7.0\,g$$
$$NaCl \quad \ldots\ldots\ldots\ldots\ldots 1.0\,g$$

10 ml of each stock solution are added to 940 ml of distilled water.

---

* For the formulae of other culture media used in the cultivation of algae and for methods and general references for the cultivation of algae see R. C. Starr, "The Culture Collection of Algae at Indiana University," *American Journal of Botany, 51* (1964), 1013–1044.

† T. R. Deason, and H. C. Bold, "Phycological Studies 1. Exploratory Studies of Texas Soil Algae," Univ. of Texas Publication, Pub. No. 6022 (1960), 70 pp.

Part II.   Four stock, trace-element solutions are prepared as follows:

1. H_3BO_3 .... 11.42 g/liter
2. $FeSO_4 \cdot 7H_2O$ .... 4.98 g/liter
   $ZnSO_4 \cdot 7H_2O$ .... 8.82 g/liter
   $MnCl_2 \cdot 4H_2O$ .... 1.44 g/liter
3. MoO_3 .... 0.71 g/liter
   $CuSO_4 \cdot 5H_2O$ .... 1.57 g/liter
   $Co(NO_3)_2 \cdot 6H_2O$ .... 0.49 g/liter
4. EDTA .... 50.0 g/liter
   KOH .... 31.0 g/liter

1.0 ml of each stock solution is added to the above Part I solution. If a solid medium is desired, 15 g of agar are added.

Trebouxia Organic Nutrient Medium—I:

Bold's Mineral Solution .... 970 ml
Proteose peptone .... 10 g
Glucose .... 20 g

Trebouxia Organic Nutrient Medium—II:

Bold's Mineral Solution .... 980 ml
Casamino acids ("vitamin-free") .. 10 g
Glucose .... 10 g

B. FUNGAL SYMBIONT*

Malt-Yeast Extract Medium:

Malt extract .... 20 g
Yeast extract .... 2 g
Agar .... 20 g
Distilled water .... 1000 ml

* For the formulae of culture media and for descriptions of culture techniques for fungi see V. G. Lilly and H. L. Barnett, *Physiology of the Fungi* (New York: McGraw-Hill, 1951), 464 pp.

For a clear liquid medium substitute 20 g of malt extract broth for the malt extract and add 2 g of yeast extract per liter of distilled water.

Lilly and Barnett's Medium:

Glucose	10.0 g
Asparagine	2.0 g
KH_2PO_4	1.0 g
$MgSO_4 \cdot 7H_2O$	0.5 g
$Fe(NO_3)_3 \cdot 9H_2O$	0.2 mg
$ZnSO_4 \cdot 7H_2O$	0.2 mg
$MnSO_4 \cdot 4H_2O$	0.1 mg
Thiamine	100 μg
Biotin	5 μg

Soil-Extract Medium:

Bold's Mineral Solution	960	ml
Soil-water*	40	ml
Agar	15	g

* Equal parts of garden soil and water are autoclaved for one hour. The mixture is allowed to cool and the liquid is then filtered until clear; autoclaved; and kept as a stock solution.

References

1. Ahmadjian, V. "A Guide for the Identification of Algae Occurring as Lichen Symbionts," *Botan. Notiser*, 111 (1958), 632–644.
   Contains a key to the genera of lichen algae and gives examples of the lichens in which they are found. Includes a list of algal names reported as lichen symbionts. Describes two methods for culturing lichen algae in order to obtain generic identifications.

2. Ahmadjian, V. "The Taxonomy and Physiology of Lichen Algae and Problems of Lichen Synthesis." (Ph.D. dissertation, Harvard University, 1959.)
   Available on loan from the Biological Laboratories' Library, Harvard University. Part I contains chapters on the isolation, culture, and description of algal symbionts, mostly *Trebouxia*; electron microscopy studies of a *Trebouxia* phycobiont; and the specificity of lichens to their algal symbionts. Part II concerns lichen synthesis. Many photographs and drawings.

3. Ahmadjian, V. "Experimental Observations on the Algal Genus *Trebouxia* de Puymaly," *Svensk Botan. Tidskr.*, 53 (1959), 71–80.
   A cytological and cultural study of isolated *Trebouxia* phycobionts with four plates of photographs. Describes the micropipette technique for isolation of algal cells from a lichen thallus.

4. Ahmadjian, V. "A Contribution toward Lichen Synthesis," *Mycologia*, 51 (1959), 56–60.
   Contains photographs that illustrate the first stages of an artificially induced lichen synthesis.

5. Ahmadjian, V. "The Lichen Association," *Bryologist*, 63 (1960), 250–254.

A discussion on the possible manner by which lichen associations first begin to form under natural conditions.

6. Ahmadjian, V. "Some New and Interesting Species of *Trebouxia*, a Genus of Lichenized Algae," *Am. J. Botany, 47* (1960), 677–683.
   Contains drawings that illustrate developmental stages of the two morphological groups of *Trebouxia* phycobionts.

7. Ahmadjian, V. "Studies on Lichenized Fungi," *Bryologist 64* (1961), 168–179.
   Describes the isolation and culture of eighteen lichen fungi. Includes information on the pH and temperature values for optimal growth, vitamin requirements, and extracellular compounds of several mycobionts.

8. Ahmadjian, V. "Investigations on Lichen Synthesis," *Am. J. Botany, 49* (1962), 277–283.
   A detailed description of the techniques and results of an experimental resynthesis of a lichen association. Contains photographs of early stages of a lichen synthesis and summaries of previous investigations on lichen synthesis.

9. Ahmadjian, V. "Lichens." In *Physiology and Biochemistry of Algae* (R. A. Lewin, ed.), (New York: Academic Press, 1962), 817–822.
   A brief review of the physiology of lichen algae.

10. Ahmadjian, V. "The Fungi of Lichens," *Sci. Am., 208* (1963), 122–132.
    A general, well-illustrated introduction to the isolation and culture of lichen fungi and the reestablishment of the symbiotic state. Photographs and drawings illustrate an artificially synthesized lichen tissue, the three major types of lichens and their methods of propagation, and the colony of an isolated mycobiont. A diagram outlines a method for isolating a lichen fungus into axenic culture.

11. Ahmadjian, V. "Further Studies on Lichenized Fungi," *Bryologist, 67* (1964), 87–98.
    (a) Isolation and culture of Hawaiian lichen fungi—includes descriptions of metabolic products, effect of various carbon sources on growth, vitamin studies, production of conidia, and lichen synthesis experiments. (b) Variability of the lichen fungus *Cladonia cristatella*—descriptions of single spore isolates of the mycobiont. (c) Utilization of different nitrogen sources by two mycobionts.

12. Ahmadjian, V. "Lichens." In *Annual Review of Microbiology, 19* (1965), 1–20.
    A review of recent experimental studies of lichen symbioses.

13. Ahmadjian, V. "Lichens." In *Symbiosis:* Vol. 1 (S. M. Henry, ed.), (New York: Academic Press, 1966), 35–97.
    A review of the physiology of the lichen symbiosis, the physiology of the isolated fungal and algal symbionts, and the physiology of the composite form.

14. AHMADJIAN, V. "Artificial Reestablishment of the Lichen *Cladonia crista-tella*," *Science, 151* (1966), 199–201.
Describes experimental procedure for the artificial synthesis of a lichen.

15. AHMADJIAN, V. "A Guide to the Algae Occurring as Lichen Symbionts: Isolation, Culture, Cultural Physiology, and Identification," *Phycologia 6* (in press).
A detailed guide with descriptions and illustrations of the different lichen algae. Also contains instructions on isolation and cultural methods. An expanded and revised version of reference no. 1.

16. AHMADJIAN, V. Unpublished results.
Results of investigations not yet published conducted in the author's laboratory at Clark University.

17. AHMADJIAN, V., and J. T. REYNOLDS. "Production of Biologically Active Compounds by Isolated Lichenized Fungi," *Science, 133* (1961), 700–701.

18. ALERTSEN, A. R., T. BRUUN, and E. HEMMER. "The Occurrence of Ergosterol in the Lichen *Cornicularia normoerica* (Gunnerus) Lynge," *Acta Chem. Scand., 16* (1962), 541–542.

19. ALEXOPOULOS, C. J. *Introductory Mycology* (2nd ed.) (New York: Wiley and Sons, 1962), 613 pp.

20. ALTMAN, P. L., and D. S. DITTMER (eds.) "Growth, Including Reproduction and Morphological Development," (Washington, D.C.: Federation of American Societies for Experimental Biology, 1962), 608 pp.
Chromosome numbers of ten lichens.

21. AM ENDE, I. "Zur Ernährungsphysiologie des Pilzes der *Xanthoria parietina*," *Arch. Mikrobiol., 15* (1950), 185–202.
Describes the isolation of an *Xanthoria parietina* into axenic culture and the influence of different carbon and nitrogen sources on spore germination and growth of the fungus.

22. ANDERSON, E., and E. D. RUDOLPH. "An Analysis of Variation in a Variable Population of *Cladonia*," *Evolution, 10* (1956), 147–156.

23. ANDERSON, K. A. "Investigations on the Development of Lichen Structures in Laboratory-Controlled Cultures." (Honors Thesis, Biology Department, Clark University, Worcester, Massachusetts, 1963).
Available on loan from Biology Department, Clark University, Worcester, Massachusetts.

24. ANDERSON, K. A., and V. AHMADJIAN. "Investigation on the Development

of Lichen Structures in Laboratory Controlled Cultures," *Svensk Botan. Tidskr., 56* (1962), 501–506.

25. Ark, P. A., A. T. Bottini, and J. P. Thompson. "Sodium Usnate as an Antibiotic for Plant Diseases," *Plant Dis. Reporter, 44* (1960), 200–203.

26. Asahina, Y. "Über den taxonomischen Wert der Flechtenstoffe," *Bot. Mag.* (Tokyo), *51* (1937), 759–764.

27. Asahina, Y., and S. Shibata. *Chemistry of Lichen Substances* (Tokyo: Japan Soc. Promotion Sci., Ueno, 1954), 240 pp.
   An outstanding reference book on lichen chemistry. Contains sections on extraction, isolation, and purification of lichen substances; microchemical determination of lichen substances; and biogenesis and antimicrobial activities of lichen metabolites. Most of the book consists of descriptions, i.e., occurrence, isolation, properties, structure, and derivatives, of lichen substances.

28. Aspinall, G. O., E. L. Hirst, and M. Warburton. "The Alkali-soluble Polysaccharides of the Lichen *Cladonia alpestris* (Reindeer Moss)," *J. Chem. Soc.* (1955), 651–655.

29. Bachmann, E. "Zur Physiologie der Krustenflechten," *Z. Botan., 14* (1922), 193–233.

30. Bachmann, F. M. "The Origin and Development of the Apothecium in *Collema pulposum* (Bernh.) Ach., *Arch. für Zellforschung, 10* (1913), 369–430.
   Contains a detailed review of the literature regarding the development of apothecia in lichens.

31. Barashkova, E. A. "Rapid Renewal of Stocks of Fodder Lichens with the Help of Growth Stimulators." (In Russian.) Problemy Severa (Problems of the North), *Akad. Nauk SSSR: Moscow, 7* (1963), 135–139. From REF ZH BIOL, 1964, No. 6V64. (Translation.)

32. Barkman, J. J. *Phytosociology and Ecology of Cryptogamic Epiphytes* (Assen, Netherlands: Van Gorcum, 1958), 628 pp.
   An important reference to investigations of lichen ecology and phytosociology. A highly detailed and comprehensive treatment.

33. Basa, K. B., and E. J. Hawrylewicz. "Life in Extraterrestrial Environments" (Illinois Institute of Technology: Armour Research Foundation, Report No. 3194–4, 1962), 29 pp.

34. Beasley, T. M., and H. E. Palmer. "Lead-210 and Polonium-210 in Biological Samples from Alaska," *Science, 152* (1966), 1062–1064.

35. Becquerel, P. "Reviviscence du *Xanthoria parietina* Desséché avec sa

Faune, Six Ans dans le Vide et Deux Semaines à −189° C. Ses Conséquences Biologiques," *Compt. rend. Acad. sci.,* 226 (1948), 1413–1415.

36. BECQUEREL, P. "La Suspension de la Vie Au-dessous de 1/20° K Absolu par Démagnétisation Adiabatique de l'Alun de Fer dans le Vide le Plus Élevé." *Compt. rend. Acad. sci.,* 231 (1950), 261–263.

37. BECQUEREL, P. "La Suspension de la Vie des Algues, Lichens, Mousses aux Confins du Zéro Absolu et Rôle de la Synérèse Réversible pour Leur Survie au Dégel Expliquant l'Existence de la Flore Polaire et des Hautes Altitudes," *Compt. rend. Acad. sci.,* 232 (1951), 22–25.

38. BEDNAR, T. W. "Physiological Studies on the Isolated Components of the Lichen *Peltigera aphthosa.*" (Ph.D. dissertation, University of Wisconsin, 1963).

39. BEDNAR, T. W., and O. HOLM-HANSEN. "Biotin Liberation by the Lichen Alga *Coccomyxa* sp. and by *Chlorella pyrenoidosa,*" *Plant and Cell Physiology,* 5 (1964), 297–303.

40. BESCHEL, R. E. "Dating Rock Surfaces by Lichen Growth and Its Application to Glaciology and Physiography (Lichenometry)." In *Geology of the Arctic* (G. O. Raasch, ed.), (Toronto: University of Toronto Press, 1961), 1044–1062.
Discusses methods of lichenometry.

41. BESSEY, E. A. *Morphology and Taxonomy of Fungi* (Philadelphia: Blakiston Co., 1950), 791 pp.

42. BLISS, L. C., and E. B. HADLEY. "Photosynthesis and Respiration of Alpine Lichens," *Am. J. Botany,* 51 (1964), 870–874.

43. BLIX, G., and H. RYDIN. "Über das Vorkommen von Ergosterin und D-Vitamin in der Renntierflechte," *Upsala Läkarefören. Förhandl.,* 37 (1932), 333–340.

44. BOGUSCH, E. R. "Isolation in Unialgal Culture of Lichen Gonidia by a Simple Plasmolysis Technique," *Plant Physiol.,* 19 (1944), 559–561.

45. BOND, G., and G. D. SCOTT. "An Examination of Some Symbiotic Systems for Fixation of Nitrogen," *Ann. Botany,* 19 (1955), 67–77.

46. BRODIE, H. J., and P. H. GREGORY. "The Action of Wind in the Dispersal of Spores from Cup-Shaped Plant Structures," *Can. J. Botany,* 31 (1953), 402–410.

47. BRODO, I. M. "Field Studies of the Effects of Ionizing Radiation on Lichens," *Bryologist,* 67 (1964), 76–87.

48. BRODO, I. M. "Studies of Growth Rates of Corticolous Lichens on Long Island, New York," *Bryologist*, 68 (1965), 451–456.

49. BROWN, R. M., D. A. LARSON, and H. C. BOLD. "Airborne Algae: Their Abundance and Heterogeneity," *Science, 143* (1964), 583–585.
Trebouxia was a frequently encountered genus from air samples. Although not stated in this study, it is probable that this alga did not occur free-living, but rather was a component of asexual dispersal units of lichens known as soredia.

50. BRUCHET, G. "Étude Chromatographique des Pigments des Chlorophycées Isolées en Culture Pure à Partir de Quelques Lichens," *Ann. Univ. Lyon*, sér. 3e, sect. C, 11–12 (1959–1960), 39–49.

51. BURKHOLDER, P. R., A. W. EVANS, I. McVEIGH, and H. K. THORTON. "Antibiotic Activity of Lichens," *Proc. National Acad. Sci.*, 30 (1944), 250–255.
Describes a method for testing antibacterial activity of lichen extracts.

52. BURKHOLDER, P. R., and A. W. EVANS. "Further Studies on the Antibiotic Activity of Lichens," *Bull. Torrey Botan. Club*, 72 (1945), 157–164.
Illustrated with photographs that show the antibacterial action of lichen extracts.

53. BURZLAFF, D. F. "The Effect of Extracts from the Lichen, *Parmelia molliuscula*, upon Seed Germination and upon the Growth Rate of Fungi," *J. Colorado-Wyoming Acad. Sci.*, 4 (1950), 56.

54. BUSTINZA, F. "Antibacterial Substances from Lichens," *Endeavour, 10* (1951), 95–99.
An excellent review article with one plate of photographs that illustrate the effect of a lichen acid and a lichen extract on different microorganisms.

55. BUSTINZA, F. "Antibiotics from Lichens." In *8ème Congr. Internatl. Bot., Rapp. and Comm. Sect. 24* (1954), 57–67.
An excellent review article.

56. BUSTINZA, F., and A. C. LOPEZ. "Contribución al Estudio de los Antibióticos Procedentes de Líquenes," *Ann. Jard. Bot. Madrid*, 7 (1948), 511–548.
Contains photographs that illustrate the antibiotic activity of usnic acid against several microorganisms.

57. BUTIN, H. "Physiologisch-ökologische Untersuchungen über den Wasserhaushalt und die Photosynthese bei Flechten," *Biol. Zentr.*, 73 (1954), 459–502.

58. Cameron, R. E. "Algae of Southern Arizona," *Revue Algologique, 4* (1963), 282–318.

Parasitism among the blue-green algae is common and is predominently true for the desert flora. Nearly all of the perennial soil algal flora can be found in the parasitized or lichenized condition.

59. Capriotti, A. "The Effects of USNO on Yeasts," *Giornale di Microbiologia, 7* (1959), 187–206.

Contains a good review of the literature on the antibiotic activities of lichen substances.

60. Castle, H., and F. Kubsch. "The Production of Usnic, Didymic, and Rhodocladonic Acids by the Fungal Component of the Lichen *Cladonia cristatella*," *Arch. Biochem., 23* (1949), 158–159.

61. Chodat, R. "Monographie d'Algues en Culture Pure," *Matér. pour la Flore Cryptogam. Suisse, 4* (1913), 1–266.

Contains a separate section on lichen algae and related forms. Describes isolation, culture, cultural morphology, and physiology of lichen phycobionts, mostly *Trebouxia*. Includes drawings of the various stages in the life histories of these algae and color illustrations of their colonies.

62. Cooke, W. B. "An Ecological Life History of *Aureobasidium pullulans* (DeBary) Arnaud," *Mycopathol. et Mycol. Appl., 12* (1959), 1–45.

63. Crombie, J. M. "On the Lichen-Gonidia Question," *Popular Sci. Rev., 13* (1874), 260–277.

An outline of some of the main features of Schwendener's lichen theory is presented along with the investigators who approved or disapproved of the theory and a description of their arguments and experiments. The intensity of Crombie's personal feelings on this theory is reflected in his closing statement in which he referred to ". . . this sensational Romance of Lichenology, or the unnatural union between a captive Algal damsel and a tyrant Fungal master."

64. Crombie, J. M. "On the Algo-Lichen Hypothesis," *J. Linn. Soc.* (Botany), *21* (1884), 259–283.

A review and discussion of the Schwendenerian theory. A treatment similar to that described in ref. no. 63.

65. Culberson, C. F. "Joint Occurrence of a Lichen Depsidone and Its Probable Depside Precursor," *Science, 143* (1964), 255–256.

66. Culberson, W. L. "Recent Literature on Lichens," *Bryologist* (1951–1966), 54–69.

Lists of current literature on all aspects of lichenology.

67. Culberson, W. L. "Lichens in a Greenhouse," *Science, 139* (1963), 40–41.

Discovery of a lichen species able to grow under the controlled conditions of a greenhouse.

68. Cuthbert, J. B. "Some Notes on the Physiology of *Teloschistes flavicans*," *Trans. Roy. Soc. S. Africa*, 19 (1931), 27–44.

69. Cuthbert, J. B. "Further Notes on the Physiology of *Teloschistes flavicans*," *Trans. Roy. Soc. S. Africa*, 22 (1934), 35–54.

70. Dahl, E. "On the Use of Lichen Chemistry in Lichen Systematics," *Revue Bryologique et Lichénologique*, 21 (1952), 119–134.

71. Dawson, E. Y. "Ecological Paradox of Coastal Peru," *Nat. Hist.*, 72 (1963), 32–37.

72. Dean, F. M., J. C. Roberts, and A. Robertson. "The Chemistry of Fungi. Part XXII. Nidulin and Nornidulin ('Ustin'): Chlorine-containing Metabolic Products of *Aspergillus nidulans*," *J. Chem. Soc.*, Part II, 1954, 1432–1439.

73. Degelius, G. "The Lichen Genus *Collema* in Europe," *Symbolae Botan. Upsalienses*, 13 (1954), 1–499.

74. De Nicola, M. G., and G. Di Benedetto. "Richerche Preliminari Sui Pigmenti Nel Ficobionte Lichenico *Trebouxia decolorans* Ahm. III. Clorofille e Carotenoidi," *Bollettino dell'Istituto di Botanica dell'Università di Catania*, 3 (1962), 22–33.
A comparative study of the pigments of a *Trebouxia* phycobiont and a free-living strain of *Trebouxia*.

75. Des Abbayes, H. *Traité de Lichénologie* (Paris: Paul Lechevalier, 1951), 217 pp.
An excellent, well-illustrated, general reference to most aspects of lichenology.

76. Des Abbayes, H. "Travaux sur les Lichens parus de 1939 à 1952," *Bull. Soc. Botan. France*, 100 (1953), 83–123.
Lists of publications, along with brief comments, on various aspects of lichenology (1939–1952). Contains about six hundred references classified by subject.

77. Di Benedetto, G., and F. Furnari. "Sulla Crescita di *Trebouxia albulescens* e di *T. humicola* Trattate con Acido β Indol-Acetico e con Acido Gibberellico," *Bollettino dell'Istituto di Botanica dell'Università di Catania*, 3 (1962), 34–38.

78. Diner, B., V. Ahmadjian, and H. Rosenkrantz. "Preliminary Fractionation of Pigments from the Lichen Fungus *Acarospora fuscata*," *Bryologist*, 67 (1964), 363–368.

79. DODGE, C. W. "Ecology and Geographical Distribution of Antarctic Lichens." In *Biologie Antarctique* (R. Carrick, M. Holdgate, and J. Prévost, eds.) (Paris: Hermann, 1964), 165–171.

80. DRAKE, B. "Untersuchungen über einige Polysaccharide der Flechten, vornehmlich das Lichenin un das neuentdeckte Pustulin," *Biochem. Z., 313* (1943), 388–399.

81. EDWARDS, R. Y., J. Soos, and R. W. RITCEY. "Quantitative Observations on Epidendric Lichens Used as Food by Caribou," *Ecology, 41* (1960), 425–431.

82. ENSGRABER, A. "Über den Einfluss der Antrocknung auf die Assimilation und Atmung von Moosen und Flechten," *Flora* (Jena), *141* (1954), 432–475.

83. ERTL., L. "Über die Lichtverhältnisse in Laubflechten," *Planta, 39* (1951), 245–270.

84. FINK, B. "The Composition of a Desert Lichen Flora," *Mycologia, 1* (1909), 87–103.

85. FINK, B. "The Nature and Classification of Lichens. -I. Views and Arguments of Botanists Concerning Classification," *Mycologia, 3* (1911), 231–269.

86. FINK, B. "The Nature and Classification of Lichens. -II. The Lichen and Its Algal Host," *Mycologia, 5* (1913), 97–166.
A presentation of arguments to support the view that lichens are fungi living in parasitic relationships with algae. Contains summaries of many investigations.

87. FINK, B. "The Rate of Growth and Ecesis in Lichens," *Mycologia, 9* (1917), 138–158.

88. FOGG, G. E. *The Metabolism of Algae* (London: Methuen, 1953), 149 pp.

89. FOGG, G. E. "Extracellular Products." In *Physiology and Biochemistry of Algae* (R. A. Lewin, ed.) (New York: Academic Press, 1962), 475–489.

90. FOLLMANN, G. "Die Durchlässigkeitseigenschaften der Protoplasten von Phycobionten aus *Cladonia furcata* (Huds.) Schrad." *Naturwissenschaften, 47* (1960), 405–406.

91. FOLLMANN, G., and M. NAKAGAVA. "Keimhemmung von Angiospermensamen durch Flechtenstoffe," *Naturwissenschaften, 50* (1963), 696–697.

92. FOLLMANN, G., and V. VILLAGRÁN. "Flechtenstoffe als Virusinhibitoren," *Naturwissenschaften, 51* (1964), 543.

92a. FOLLMANN, G., and V. VILLAGRÁN. "Flechtenstoffe und Zellpermeabilität," Zeitschrift für *Naturforschung, 20b* (1965), 723.

93. FOSTER, J. W. *Chemical Activities of Fungi* (New York: Academic Press, 1949), 648 pp.

94. FOX, C. H. "Studies on the Biology of the Isolated Components of the Lichen *Ramalina ecklonii.*" (M.A. thesis, Trinity University, San Antonio, Texas, 1965).
    Describes isolation, culture, and cultural physiology of the fungal and algal symbionts of *Ramalina ecklonii.* Includes experiment which demonstrated the *in vitro* transfer of metabolic substances from the lichen alga to the lichen fungus.

95. FOX, C. H. 1965. Unpublished Results.

96. FREY, E. "Die Spezifizität der Flechtengonidien," *Ber. Schweiz. Botan. Ges., 41* (1932), 180–198.

97. FREY, E. *Die Flechtenflora und-Vegetation des Nationalparks im Unterengadin II. Die Entwicklung der Flechtenvegetation auf photogrammetrisch kontrollierten Dauerflächen,* Vol. 6 (Liestal: Druck Lüdin AG, 1959), 41. pp. 241–319.

98. FREY, R. "Chitin und Zellulose in Pilzzellwänden," *Ber. Schweiz. Botan. Ges., 60* (1950), 199–230.

99. FRITSCH, F. E., and F. M. HAINES. "The Moisture-relations of Terrestrial Algae. II. The Changes during Exposure to Drought and Treatment with Hypertonic Solutions," *Ann. Botany, 37* (1923), 683–728.

100. FRY, E. J. "The Mechanical Action of Corticolous Lichens," *Ann. Botany, 40* (1926), 397–417.

101. FRY, E. J. "The Mechanical Action of Crustaceous Lichens on Substrata of Shale, Schist, Gneiss, Limestone and Obsidian," *Ann. Botany, 41* (1927), 437–460.

102. FURNARI, F., and F. LUCIANI. "Esperienze Sulla Crescita dei Micobionti in *Sarcogyne similis* e *Acarospora fuscata* in Coltura Pura su Vari Substrati," *Bollettino dell'Istituto di Botanica dell' Università di Catania, 3* (1962), 39–47.

103. GALUN, M. "Autecological and Synecological Observations on Lichens of the Negev, Israel," *Israel J. Botany, 12* (1963), 179–186.

104. GEITLER, L. "Beiträge zur Kenntnis der Flechtensymbiose. VI. Die Verbindung von Pilz und Alge bei den Pyrenopsidaceen *Synalissa, Thyrea, Peccania* und *Psorotichia*," *Arch. für Protistenkunde*, 88 (1937), 161–179.

105. GEITLER, L. "Über Haustorien bei Flechten und über *Myrmecia Biatorellae* in *Psora globifera*," *Öster. Botan. Z.*, 110 (1963), 270–280.

106. GORHAM, E. "A Comparison of Lower and Higher Plants as Accumulators of Radioactive Fall-out," *Can. J. Botany*, 37 (1959), 327–329.

107. GREGORY, P. H. *The Microbiology of the Atmosphere* (London: Leonard Hill, 1961), 251 pp.

108. GROSS, M., and V. AHMADJIAN. "The Effects of L-Amino Acids on the Growth of Two Species of Lichen Fungi," *Svensk Botan. Tidskr.*, 60 (1966), 74–80.

109. GUSTAFSON, F. G. "A Study of Riboflavin, Thiamine, Niacin and Ascorbic Acid Content of Plants in Northern Alaska," *Bull. Torrey Botan. Club*, 81 (1954), 313–322.

110. HALE, M. E. "First Report on Lichen Growth Rate and Succession at Aton Forest, Connecticut," *Bryologist*, 57 (1954), 244–247.

111. HALE, M. E. "Conidial Stage of the Lichen Fungus *Buellia stillingiana* and Its Relation to *Sporidesmium folliculatum*," *Mycologia*, 49 (1957), 417–419.

112. HALE, M. E. "Vitamin Requirements of Three Lichen Fungi," *Bull. Torrey Botan. Club*, 85 (1958), 182–187.

113. HALE, M. E. "Studies on Lichen Growth Rate and Succession," *Bull. Torrey Botan. Club*, 86 (1959), 126–129.

114. HALE, M. E. *Lichen Handbook* (Washington, D.C.: Smithsonian Institution Pub. 4434, 1961), 178 pp.
    A general, well-illustrated introduction to lichens. The topics covered best are lichen chemistry and taxonomy. Techniques for the isolation and identification of lichen acids and keys for the identification of lichens in the forests of eastern North America are included. This book will give the reader a simple and brief introduction to the basic nature and physiology of lichens.

115. HALL, E. A., F. KAVANAGH, and I. N. ASHESHOV. "Action of Forty-Five Antibacterial Substances on Bacterial Viruses," *Antibiot. and Chemotherapy*, 1 (1951), 369–378.

116. HARDER, R., and E. UEBELMESSER. "Über die Beeinflussung niederer Erdphycomyceten durch Flechten," *Arch. Mikrobiol.*, 31 (1958), 82–86.

117. HARLEY, J. L., and D. C. SMITH. "Sugar Absorption and Surface Carbohydrase Activity of *Peltigera polydactyla* (Neck.) Hoffm.," *Ann. Botany*, 20 (1956), 513–543.

118. HARRIS, N. J. 1961. "Some Investigations on the Pharmacological Activity of Usnic Acid." (Honors thesis, Biology Department, Clark University, Worcester, Massachusetts.)
    Available on loan from Biology Department, Clark University, Worcester, Massachusetts.

119. HAUSMAN, E. H. "Measurements of the Annual Growth-Rate of Two Species of Rock Lichens," *Bull. Torrey Botan. Club*, 75 (1948), 116–117.

120. HAYNES, F. N. "Lichens." In *Viewpoints in Biology* (J. D. Carthy and C. L. Duddington, eds.) (London: Butterworths, 1964), Vol. 3, 64–115.
    A review on lichens that contains separate sections on morphology and anatomy, reproduction, physiology, symbiosis, chemistry, systematics, ecology-phytosociology-phytogeography, and economic uses.

121. HEATWOLE, H. "Moisture Exchange between the Atmosphere and Some Lichens of the Genus *Cladonia*," *Mycologia*, 58 (1966), 148–156.

122. HEILMAN, A. S., and A. J. SHARP. "A Probable Antibiotic Effect of Some Lichens on Bryophytes," *Revue Bryologique et Lichénologique*, 32 (1963), 215.

123. HENRICI, M. "Zweigipflige Assimilationskurven. Mit spezieller Berücksichtigung der Photosynthese von alpinen phanerogamen Schattenpflanzen und Flechten," *Verhandl. Naturforsch. Ges. Basel*, 32 (1921), 107–171.

124. HENRIKSSON, E. "Nitrogen Fixation by a Bacteria-free, Symbiotic *Nostoc* Strain Isolated from *Collema*," *Physiol. Plantarum*, 4 (1951), 542–545.
    Includes a description of the technique used in isolating the *Nostoc* phycobiont of *Collema* into axenic culture.

125. HENRIKSSON, E. "Studies in the Physiology of the Lichen *Collema*. I. The Production of Extracellular Nitrogenous Substances by the Algal Partner under Various Conditions," *Physiol. Plantarum*, 10 (1957), 943–948.

126. HENRIKSSON, E. "Studies in the Physiology of the Lichen *Collema*. II. A Preliminary Report on the Isolated Fungal Partner with Special Regard to Its Behavior When Growing Together with the Symbiotic Alga," *Svensk Botan. Tidskr.*, 52 (1958), 391–396.

127. HENRIKSSON, E. "Studies in the Physiology of the Lichen *Collema*. III. The Occurrence of an Inhibitory Action of the Phycobiont on the Growth of the Mycobiont," *Physiol. Plantarum*, 13 (1960), 751–754.

128. HENRIKSSON, E. "Studies in the Physiology of the Lichen *Collema*. IV. The Occurrence of Polysaccharides and Some Vitamins Outside the Cells of the Phycobiont, *Nostoc* sp." *Physiol. Plantarum, 14* (1961), 813–817.

129. HENRIKSSON, E. "Studies in the Physiology of the Lichen *Collema*. V. Effect of Medium, Temperature, and pH on Growth of the Mycobiont," *Svensk Botan. Tidskr., 58* (1964), 361–370.

130. HENRIKSSON, E. "Studies in the Physiology of the Lichen *Collema*." (Doctoral dissertation, University of Uppsala, Uppsala, Sweden.) *Acta Universitatis Upsaliensis*, Abstracts of Uppsala Dissertations in Science, 38 (1964), 3–13.

131. HENRY. S. M. (ed.). *Symbiosis, I, II* (New York: Academic Press, 1966), 478 pp., 400 pp.
     Detailed treatments of different symbiotic systems with emphasis on the biochemical and physiological aspects of symbiosis.

132. HESS, D. "Über die Papierchromatographie von Flechtenstoffen," *Planta,* 52 (1958), 65–76.
     Describes methods for the localization and identification of lichen acids.

133. HESS, D. "Untersuchungen über die Bildung von Phenolkörpern durch isolierte Flechtenpilze." *Zeitschrift für Naturforschung, 14b* (1959), 345–347.

134. HESS, D. "Untersuchungen über die hemmende Wirkung von Extrakten aus Flechtenpilzen auf das Wachstum von *Neurospora crassa*," *Zeitschrift für Botanik, 48* (1959), 136–142.

135. HESS, D. "Flechtenpilze," *Mikrokosmos, 50* (1961), 40–45.
     Describes the isolation, culture, anatomy, and morphology, as well as the extracellular chemical substances of lichen fungi. Includes photographs that illustrate the lichenized and non-lichenized states of two mycobionts.

136. HILITZER, A. "Réception et Évaporation de l'Eau chez le Thalle des Lichens," *Ceska Akademie ved a umeni v Praze, Bulletin International,* 28 (1927), 228–245.

137. HOOGENHOUT, H., and J. AMESZ. "Growth Rates of Photosynthetic Microorganisms in Laboratory Cultures," *Arch. Mikrobiol., 50* (1965), 10–24.

138. HORSFALL, J. G. *Principles of Fungicidal Action* (Waltham, Massachusetts: Chronica Botanica, 1956), 280 pp.

139. INGOLD, C. T. *Dispersal in Fungi* (Oxford: Clarendon Press, 1964), 208 pp.
     Discusses the methods and mechanisms of spore discharge and dispersal in fungi.

140. JAAG, O. "Recherches Expérimentales sur les Gonidies des Lichens Appartenant aux Genres *Parmelia* et *Cladonia*," *Bull. Soc. Botan. Genève*, 21 (1929), 1–119.

Detailed investigations on the isolation, culture, cultural morphology, physiology, and cytology of *Trebouxia* phycobionts from *Cladonia* and *Parmelia*. Presents a historical review of the investigations on the culture of lichen algae. Comparative studies of the phycobionts from both lichen genera were made as well as an attempt to study the specificity of algae to certain lichens. Contains 6 plates of photographs that illustrate colonies of *Trebouxia* (= *Cystococcus*) phycobionts and drawings which show the developmental stages of these algae.

141. JOHNSON, G. T. "Ascogonia and Spermatia of *Stereocaulon*," *Mycologia*, 46 (1954), 339–345.

142. JOHNSON, R. B., G. FELDOTT, and H. A. LARDY. "The Mode of Action of the Antibiotic, Usnic Acid," *Arch. Biochem.*, 28 (1950), 317–323.

143. JOHNSON, T. W., and F. K. SPARROW. *Fungi in Oceans and Estuaries* (Weinham: J. Cramer, 1961), 668 pp.

Contains descriptions of fungal-algal associations which resemble lichens.

144. JUMELLE, H. "Recherches Physiologiques sur les Lichens," *Rev. Gén. Botan.*, 4 (1892), 49–64, 103–121, 305–320.

145. KARLING, J. S. "A Preliminary Contribution to the Structure and Development of *Coenogonium Linkii*," *Ann. Botany*, 48 (1934), 823–855.

146. KELE, R. A. 1964. "Isolation of the Mycobiont and Phycobiont of an Underwater Lichen, *Hydrothyria venosa*." (Honors thesis, Biology Department, Clark University, Worcester, Massachusetts.)

Available on loan from Biology Department, Clark University, Worcester, Massachusetts.

147. KERSHAW, K. A. "Lichens," *Endeavour*, 22 (1963), 65–69.

148. KLOSA, J. "Evosin, ein neues Antibioticum aus Flechten," *Das Deutsche Gesundheitswesen (Zeitschrift für Medizin)*, 4 (1949), 691.

149. KOFLER, L. and F. BOUZON. "Émission et Germination des Spores Chez Quelques Champignons des Lichens," *Comptes Rendus du Congrès des Soc. Savantes*, 85 (1960), 389–399.

A study of the ejection and germination of the spores of lichen fungi and some factors that influence these processes.

150. KOLUMBE, E. "Untersuchungen über die Wasserdampfaufnahme der Flechten," *Planta*, 3 (1927), 734–757.

151. LAL, B. M., and K. R. RAO. "The Food Value of Some Indian Lichens," *J. Sci. and Indus. Res.*, 15C (1956), 71–73.

152. Lamb, I. M. "Symbiosis: Part II, The Remarkable Lichens," *Nat. Hist.*, 47 (1958), 86–93.
A general introduction to lichens with photographs that illustrate the three basic types of lichens, i.e., crustose, foliose, and fruticose.

153. Lamb, I. M. "Lichens," *Sci. Am.*, 201 (1959), 144–156.
A general, well-illustrated, popular treatment of lichens with drawings and photographs of different types of lichen thalli and the means by which they propagate. The cover of the journal is a color drawing that shows a naturally occurring specimen of the lichen *Cladonia cristatella* and cultures of its separated algal and fungal symbionts.

154. Lange, O. L. "Hitze- und Trockenresistenz der Flechten in Beziehung zu ihrer Verbreitung," *Flora* (Jena), 140 (1953), 39–97.

155. Lange, O. L. "Einige Messungen zum Wärmehaushalt poikilohydrer Flechten und Moose," *Arch. Meteorol., Geophys. u. Bioklimat.*, Ser. B, 5 (1954), 182–190.

156. Lange, O. L. "Die Photosynthese der Flechten bei tiefen Temperaturen und nach Frostperioden," *Ber. Deut. Botan. Ges.*, 75 (1962), 351–352.

157. Lange, O. L. "Der CO_2-Gaswechsel von Flechten bei tiefen Temperaturen," *Planta*, 64 (1965), 1–19.

158. Lange, O. L. "Der CO_2-Gaswechsel von Flechten nach Erwärmung im feuchten Zustand," *Ber. Deut, Botan. Ges.*, 78 (1965), 441–454.

159. Lange, O. L., and A. Bertsch. "Photosynthese der Wüstenflechte *Ramalina maciformis* nach Wasserdampfaufnahme aus dem Luftraum," *Naturwissenschaften*, 52 (1965), 215–216.

160. Lange, O. L., and H. Metzner. "Lichtabhängiger Kohlenstoff-Einbau in Flechten bei tiefen Temperaturen," *Naturwissenschaften*, 52 (1965), 191–192.

161. Lazarev, N. V., and V. P. Savicz (eds.). *The New Antibiotic Binan, or the Sodium Salt of Usnic Acid* (*Botanical and Medical Investigations*) (in Russian) (Moscow-Leningrad: Akademiia Nauk SSSR, Botanicheskii Institut im. V. L. Komarova, 1957), 224 pp.

161a. Lazo, W. R. "An Experimental Association between *Chlorella xanthella* and a *Streptomyces*," *Am. J. Botany*, 53 (1966), 105–107.

162. Leonian, L. H., and V. G. Lilly. "Is Heteroauxin a Growth Promoting Substance?" *Am. J. Botany*, 24 (1937), 135–139.

163. Letrouit-Galinou, M.-A. "Étude du Développement des Apothécies chez le Discolichen *Buellia canescens* (Dicks.) D. Notrs.," *Bull. Soc. Botan. France*, 108 (1961), 281–290.

164. LETROUIT-GALINOU, M.-A. "Sur le Développement des Podétions et des Apothécies du Lichen *Cladonia Floerkeana* (Fr.) Sommf.," *Bull. Soc. Botan. France, 111* (1964), 248–254.

165. LILLY, V. G., and H. L. BARNETT. *Physiology of the Fungi* (New York: McGraw-Hill, 1951), 464 pp.

166. LINDBERG, B., C. A. WACHTMEISTER, and B. WICKBERG. "Studies on the Chemistry of Lichens. II. Umbilicin, an Arabitol Galactoside from *Umbilicaria pustulata* (L.) Hoffm.," *Acta Chem. Scand., 6* (1952), 1052–1055.

167. LINDBERG, B., A. MISIORNY, and C. A. WACHTMEISTER. "Studies on the Chemistry of Lichens. IV. Investigation of the Low-molecular Carbohydrate Constituents of Different Lichens," *Acta Chem. Scand., 7* (1953), 591–595.

168. LINKOLA, K. "Messungen über den jährlichen Längenzuwachs einiger *Parmelia-* und *Parmeliopsis-*Arten," *Societes Pro Fauna et Flora Fennica, Meddelanden, 44* (1918), 153–158.

169. LLANO, G. A. "Lichens. Their Biological and Economic Significance," *Bot. Rev., 10* (1944), 1–65.
    An excellent review article on many aspects of lichenology, in particular, the economic uses of lichens.

170. LLANO, G. A. "Economic Uses of Lichens" (Washington, D.C.: U.S. Gov. Printing Office, 1951) from the Smithsonian Report for 1950, pp. 385–422.
    A general discussion of most of the economic uses of lichens.

171. LLANO, G. A. "Utilization of Lichens in the Arctic and Subarctic," *Econ. Botany, 10* (1956), 367–392.

172. LOUNAMAA, J. "Trace Elements in Plants Growing Wild on Different Rocks in Finland. A Semi-Quantitative Spectrographic Survey," *Ann. Botan. Soc. Zool. Botan. Fenn. "Vanamo," 29* (1956), 1–196.

173. LOUNAMAA, K. J. "Studies on the Content of Iron, Manganese and Zinc in Macrolichens," *Ann. Botan. Fennici, 2* (1965), 127–137.

174. MANCO, P. A. "A Study of Two Lichen Phycobionts of the Genus *Trebouxia* in Culture. (M.S. thesis, University of Tennessee, 1962, Knoxville, Tennessee.)

175. MARSHAK, A., and J. FAGER. "Prevention of Nuclear Fusion and Mitosis and Inhibition of Desoxyribonuclease by D-Usnic Acid," *J. Cellular Comp. Physiol., 35* (1950), 317–329.

176. Mattick, F. "Lichenes. Flechten." In *Engler's Syllabus der Pflanzenfamilien* (Berlin: Borntraege, 1954), I, Chap. 13, 204–218.
Classification and descriptions of the various lichen classes, orders, and families.

177. Miller, E. V., C. E. Griffin, T. Schaefers, and M. Gordon. "Two Types of Growth Inhibitors in Extracts of *Umbilicaria papulosa*," *Botan. Gaz., 126* (1965), 100–107.

178. Miller, M. W. *The Pfizer Handbook of Microbial Metabolites* (New York: McGraw-Hill, 1961), 772 pp.
Includes lichen substances.

179. Mish, L. B. "Biological Studies of Symbiosis between the Alga and Fungus in the Rock Lichen *Umbilicaria papulosa*." (Ph.D. dissertation, Harvard University, 1953, Cambridge, Massachusetts.)
Available on loan from the Biological Laboratories' Library, Harvard University.

180. Mitchell, J. C., and R. H. Champion. "Human Allergy to Lichens," *Bryologist, 68* (1965), 116–118.

181. Moissejeva, E. N. *Biochemical Properties of Lichens and their Practical Importance* (In Russian with English summary) (Moscow: Izdatel'stvo Akademiia Nauk CCCR, 1961), 82 pp.

182. Möller, A. "Ueber die Cultur flechtenbildender Ascomyceten ohne Algen." (Doctoral dissertation, Königliche Akad. Münster, 1887.)

183. Moore, R. T., and J. H. McAlear. "Fine Structure of Mycota. 2. Demonstration of the Haustoria of Lichens," *Mycologia, 52* (1960), 805–807.

184. Moreau, F. *Les Lichens. Morphologie, Biologie, Systématique* (Paris: Paul Lechevalier, 1928), 144 pp.

185. Moreau, F., and F. Moreau. "Les Phénomènes Cytologiques de la Reproduction chez les Champignons des Lichens," *Botaniste, 20* (1928), 1–67.

186. Mosbach, K. "On the Biosynthesis of Lichen Substances. Part 1. The Depside Gyrophoric Acid," *Acta Chem. Scand., 18* (1964), 329–334.

187. Mosbach, K. Correction to "On the Biosynthesis of Lichen Substances. Part 1. The Depside Gyrophoric Acid." *Acta Chem. Scand., 18* (1964), 2013.

188. Mosbach, K. "On the Biosynthesis of Lichen Substances. Part 2. The Pulvic Acid Derivative Vulpinic Acid," *Biochem. Biophys. Res. Commun., 17* (1964), 363–367.

189. MOSBACH, K. "Studies on the Biosynthesis of Aromatic Compounds in Fungi and Lichens." (Doctoral dissertation, University of Lund, 1964, Lund, Sweden.)

190. MOSBACH, K., and U. EHRENSVÄRD. "Studies on Lichen Enzymes Part I. Preparation and Properties of a Depside Hydrolysing Esterase and of Orsellinic Acid Decarboxylase," *Biochem. Biophys. Res. Commun.*, 22 (1966), 145–150.

191. MOYCHO, W., M. GUBAŃSKI, and T. KEDZIORA. "Tobacco Mosaic Virus (TMV) Inhibitors in Lichens," *Bull. Acad. Polonaise Sci. Ser. Biol.*, 8 (1960), 209–212.

192. NEUBAUER, H. F. "Zur Ökologie von in Buchenkronen epiphytisch lebenden Flechten," *Beitr. Biol. Pflanz.*, 25 (1938), 273–289.

193. OTT, E. "Über den Einfluss von Flechtensäuren auf die Keimung verschiedener Baumarten," *Schweiz. Zeitschr. für Forstwesen*, 112 (1961), 303–304.

194. OZENDA, P. "Lichens." In *Handbuch der Pflanzenanatomie*, 6 (Berlin: Borntraege, 1963), 199 pp.
    A highly detailed and well-illustrated treatment of lichen anatomy and morphology with sections on the fungal and algal symbionts, vegetative anatomy, and the reproductive structures.

195. PALMER, H. E., W. C. HANSON, B. I. GRIFFIN, and W. C. ROESCH. "Cesium-137 in Alaskan Eskimos," *Science*, 142 (1963), 64–66.

196. PARKER, B. C., and H. C. BOLD. "Biotic Relationships between Soil Algae and Other Microorganisms," *Am. J. Botany*, 48 (1961), 185–197.
    Detailed studies of the casual mechanisms of the associative effects of two fungal-algal associations.

197. PEIRCE, G. J. "The Relation of Fungus and Alga in Lichens," *Am. Naturalist*, 34 (1900), 245–253.

198. PERLIN, A. S., and S. SUZUKI. "The Structure of Lichenin: Selective Enzymolysis Studies," *Can. J. Chemistry*, 40 (1962), 50–56.

199. PHILLIPS, H. C. "Growth Rate of *Parmelia isidiosa* (Müll. Arg.) Hale," *J. Tennessee Acad. Sci.*, 38 (1963), 95–96.

200. PLATT, R. B., and F. P. AMSLER. "A Basic Method for the Immediate Study of Lichen Growth Rates and Succession," *J. Tennessee Acad. Sci.*, 30 (1955), 177–183.

201. PLESSL, A. "Über die Beziehungen von Haustorientypus und Organisationshöhe bei Flechten," *Öster. Botan. Z.*, 110 (1963), 194–269.

202. POELT, J., and F. OBERWINKLER. "Zur Kenntnis der flechtenbildenden Blätterpilze der Gattung *Omphalina,*" *Öster. Botan. Z., 111* (1964), 393–401.

203. PRINGSHEIM, E. G. *Pure Cultures of Algae* (London: Cambridge University Press, 1946), 119 pp.
Describes techniques for obtaining and maintaining axenic cultures of algae. Includes chapters on the implements and media for growing algae and the pipetting or washing method for algal isolations.

204. PUEYO, G. "Presénce de Mannitol et d'Arabitol dans de Nouvelles Espèces de Lichens. Un Hétéroside Nouveau (Peltigéroside) dans *Peltigera horizontalis* Hoffm," *Revue Bryologique et Lichénologique, 29* (1960), 124–129.

205. PUEYO, G. "Recherches sur la Nature et l'Évolution des Glucides Solubles chez Quelques Lichens du Bassin Parisien," *Année Biol., 36* (1960), 117–169.

206. PUYMALY, A. DE. "Les Isidies des Lichens: Leur Nature et Leur Role," *Le Botaniste, 48* (1965), 237–247.

207. QUISPEL, A. "The Lichenisation of Aerophilic Algae," *Proc. Nederl. Akademie Van Wetenschappen, C 45* (1942), 276–282.
Isolation, culture, and cultural physiology of unknown fungi from algal covers.

208. QUISPEL, A. "The Mutual Relations between Algae and Fungi in Lichens," *Rec. Trav. Botan. Néerl., 40* (1943–1945), 413–541.
A study of the physiology of two lichen fungi, three *Trebouxia* phycobionts, and unidentified fungi isolated from algal covers. Separate chapters deal with the isolation and description of the symbionts, their growth requirements, production of lichen acids, and water relations. Lichen synthesis experiments are described, as well as some considerations on the mutual relationships between a fungus and an alga in a lichen symbiosis. Literature reviews are given for each chapter topic.

209. QUISPEL, A. "Some Theoretical Aspects of Symbiosis," *Antonie van Leeuwenhoek, 17* (1951), 69–80.
Discusses the concept and evolution of symbiosis.

210. QUISPEL, A. "Lichens." In *Handbuch der Pflanzenphysiologie* (W. Ruhland, ed.) (Berlin: Springer, 1959), *11,* 577–604.
A review on the isolation, culture, nutrition, and physiology of the fungal and algal symbionts and the physiology and symbiotic nature of the composite forms.

211. QUISPEL, A. "Respiration of Lichens." In *Handbuch der Pflanzenphysiologie* (W. Ruhland, ed.) (Berlin: Springer, 1960), *12,* Part 2, 455–460.
A review article.

211a. RAMAKRISHNAN, S., and S. S. SUBRAMANIAN. "Amino-Acids of *Lobaria subisidiosa, Umbilicaria pustulata, Parmelia nepalensis and Ramalina sinensis," Current Sci.* (India), *35* (1966), 124–125.

212. RAO, D. N., and F. LEBLANC. "A Possible Role of Atranorin in the Lichen Thallus," *Bryologist, 68* (1965), 284–289.

213. RAO, D. N., and F. LEBLANC. "Effects of Sulfur Dioxide on the Lichen Algae, with Special Reference to Chlorophyll," *Bryologist, 69* (1966), 69–75.

214. RATHS, H. "Experimentelle Untersuchungen mit Flechtengonidien aus der Familie der Caliciaceen," *Ber. Schweiz. Botan. Ges., 48* (1938), 329–416.

    A cultural study of *Trebouxia, Chlorella, Stichococcus,* and *Trentepohlia* phycobionts. Contains six plates of photographs that illustrate size and color differences both of the different phycobiont colonies and of the colonies of one phycobiont grown under different conditions of temperature and media.

215. RIED, A. "Stoffwechsel und Verbreitungsgrenzen von Flechten. II. Wasser- und Assimilationshaushalt, Entquellungs- und Submersionsresistenz von Krustenflechten benachbarter Standorte," *Flora* (Jena), *149* (1960), 345–385.

216. RIED, A. "Thallusbau und Assimilationshaushalt von Laub- und Krustenflechten," *Biol. Zentr., 79* (1960), 129–151.

217. RIED, A. "Nachwirkungen der Entquellung auf den Gaswechsel von Krustenflechten," *Biol. Zentr., 79* (1960), 657–678.

218. ROMS, E. G. "On the Constancy of Algae as a Component of the Thallus of Certain Pulvocarpous Lichens," (In Ukrainian with English summary.) *Ukrayins'k Botan, Zhur., 20* (1963), 57–60.

219. RUDOLPH, E. D. "Lichen Ecology and Microclimate Studies at Cape Hallett, Antarctica," *Proc. Third Intern. Biometerological Congress* (Oxford: Pergamon Press, 1966, in press).

220. RYDZAK, J. "A Method of Studying Growth in Lichens," *Annales Universitatis Mariae Curie-Skłodowska, C 10* (1956), 87–91.

221. RYDZAK, J. "Investigations on the Growth Rate of Lichens," *Annales Universitatis Mariae Curie-Skłodowska, C 16* (1961), 1–13.

222. SALO, A., and J. K. MIETTINEN. "Strontium-90 and Caesium-137 in Arctic Vegetation during 1961," *Nature, 201* (1964), 1177–1179.

223. SANTESSON, R. "Foliicolous Lichens I." *Symbolae Botan. Upsalienses, 12* (1952), 1–590.

    Contains an excellent review and discussion on the taxonomy of lichen fungi.

224. Santesson, R. "The New Systematics of Lichenized Fungi," *Proceedings of the Seventh International Botanical Congress* (Stockholm, 1950), 1953, 809–810.
A brief, preliminary scheme of the taxonomical position of lichen fungi.

225. Schaede, R. "Die Flechten." In *Die Pflanzlichen Symbiosen* (3rd ed. by F. H. Meyer). (Stuttgart: Gustav Fischer, 1962), 90–125.
A general, well-illustrated review of the biology of lichen symbioses.

226. Schatz, A. "Soil Microorganisms and Soil Chelation. The Pedogenic Action of Lichens and Lichen Acids," *Agr. Food Chem.*, *11* (1963), 112–118.

227. Schatz, A., V. Schatz, G. S. Trelawny, and K. Barth. "Biochemical Studies of Lichens. I. Endogenous and Substrate Oxidation by *Cladonia rangiferina*," *Proc. Pennsylvania Acad. Sci.*, *30* (1956), 54–61.

228. Schatz, A., E. Schalscha, and V. Schatz. "Biochemical and Ecologic Interrelationships in Lichens," *Am. J. Botany*, *51* (1964), 678 (Abstract).

229. Schiman, H. "Beiträge zur Lebensgeschichte Homoeomerer and Heteromerer Cyanophyceen-Flechten," *Öster. Botan. Z.*, *104* (1957), 409–453.

230. Scholander, P. F., W. Flagg, V. Walters, and L. Irving. "Respiration in Some Arctic and Tropical Lichens in Relation to Temperature," *Am. J. Botany*, *39* (1952), 707–713.

231. Scholander, P. F., W. Flagg, R. J. Hock, and L. Irving. "Studies on the Physiology of Frozen Plants and Animals in the Arctic," *J. Cellular Comp. Physiol.*, *42* (1953) (Suppl. 1), 1–56.

232. Schwendener, S. *In* "Protokoll der Botanischen Sektion," *Verhand. Schweiz. Naturforsch. Ges. 51* (1867), 88–91.

233. Schwendener, S. "Die Algentypen der Flechtengonidien," *Programm für die Rectorsfeier der Universität Basel*, *4* (1869), 1–42.

234. Schwendener, S. "Erörterung zur Gonidienfrage," *Flora*, N.R., *30* (1872), 161–166, 177–183, 193–202, 225–234.

235. Scofield, H. T., and L. E. Yarman. "Some Investigations of the Water Relations of Lichens," *Ohio J. Sci.*, *43* (1943), 139–146.

236. Scott, G. D. "Further Investigation of Some Lichens for Fixation of Nitrogen," *New Phytologist*, *55* (1956), 111–116.
Contains a review on the presence of *Azotobacter* in lichens.

237. Scott, G. D. "Lichen Terminology," *Nature*, *179* (1957), 486–487.
Introduction of two new (now accepted) terms in lichenology: phycobiont = a lichen alga; mycobiont = a lichen fungus.

238. Scott, G. D. "Observations on Spore Discharge and Germination in *Peltigera praetextata* (Flk.) Vain," *Lichenologist, 1* (1959), 109–111.

239. Scott, G. D. "Studies of the Lichen Symbiosis. I. The Relationship between Nutrition and Moisture Content in the Maintenance of the Symbiotic State," *New Phytologist, 59* (1960), 374–381.

240. Scott, G. D. "The Lichen Symbiosis." In *Recent Studies of Lichens, Advan. Sci.* (British Assoc.), *31* (1964), 244–248.
     Discussion of some of the problems involved in a study of the lichen symbiosis. Contains a description of the early stages of the natural development of *Solorina saccata*.

241. Scott, G. D. "Studies of the Lichen Symbiosis. 2. Ascospore Germination in the Genus *Peltigera*," *Z. für Allgemeine Mikrobiologie, 4* (1964), 326–336.
     Spore germination occurred only in an extract of the phycobiont (*Nostoc*) and spore rupture was shown to be related to the presence of vitamins. Describes techniques for collecting spores and also for making interspecific and intergeneric grafts of lichens.

242. Scotter, G. W. "Productivity of Arboreal Lichens and Their Possible Importance to Barren-Ground Caribou (*Rangifer arcticus*)," *Arch. Soc. Zool. Bot. Fenn.* "*Vanamo,*" *16* (1962), 155–161.

243. Scotter, G. W. "Growth Rates of *Cladonia alpestris, C. mitis,* and *C. rangiferina* in the Taltson River Regions, N.W.T.," *Can. J. Botany, 41* (1963), 1199–1202.

244. Shibata, S. "Especial Compounds of Lichens." In *Handbuch der Pflanzenphysiologie* (W. Ruhland, ed.) (Berlin: Springer, 1958), *10,* 560–623.
     A review of lichen substances. Includes sections on biosynthesis and biological activity of lichen compounds.

245. Shibata, S. "Lichen Substances." In *Modern Methods of Plant Analysis* (K. Paech and M. V. Tracey, eds.) (Berlin: Springer, 1963), *6,* 155–193.
     An excellent review article. Describes in detail the techniques for the extraction, isolation, purification, and identification of lichen substances. Gives a general survey of the types of lichen substances, with several photographs of the crystals of different lichen acids.

245a. Shibata, S. "Biogenetical and Chemotaxonomical Aspects of Lichen Substances." In *Beiträge zur Biochemie und Physiologie von Naturstoffen* (Jena: Gustav Fischer, 1965), 451–465.

246. Shibata, S., and H.-C. Chiang. "The Structures of Cryptochlorophaeic Acids and Merochlorophaeic Acid," *Phytochemistry, 4* (1965), 133–139.

247. Shields, L. M., C. Mitchell, and F. Drouet. "Alga- and Lichen-Stabi-

lized Surface Crusts as Soil Nitrogen Sources," *Am. J. Botany, 44* (1957), 489–498.

248. SHIELDS, L. M., and L. W. DURRELL. "Algae in Relation to Soil Fertility," *Bot. Rev., 30* (1964), 92–128.
  Viability of algae after years of dry storage.

249. SJÖSTRÖM, A. G. M., and L. E. ERICSON. "The Occurrence in Lichens of the Folic Acid, Folinic Acid, and Vitamin B_{12} Group of Factors," *Acta Chem. Scand., 7* (1953), 870–872.

250. SMITH, A. L. *Lichens* (London: Cambridge Univ. Press, 1921), 464 pp.
  A detailed treatment of most aspects of lichenology. A classic book which, despite its date of publication, still remains an important reference book in the field of lichenology.

251. SMITH, D. C. "Studies in the Physiology of Lichens. 1. The Effects of Starvation and of Ammonia Absorption upon the Nitrogen Content of *Peltigera polydactyla*," *Ann. Botany, 24* (1960), 52–62.

252. SMITH, D. C. "Studies in the Physiology of Lichens. 2. Absorption and Utilization of Some Simple Organic Nitrogen Compounds by *Peltigera polydactyla*," *Ann. Botany, 24* (1960), 172–185.

253. SMITH, D. C. "Studies in the Physiology of Lichens. 3. Experiments with Dissected Discs of *Peltigera polydactyla*," *Ann. Botany, 24* (1960), 186–199.

254. SMITH, D. C. "The Physiology of *Peltigera polydactyla* (Neck.) Hoffm.," *Lichenologist, 1* (1961), 209–226.

255. SMITH, D. C. "The Biology of Lichen Thalli," *Biol. Rev., 37* (1962), 537–570.
  An excellent review of the physiology of lichen thalli, which includes separate sections on water relations, respiration, photosynthesis, nutrition and metabolism, chemistry, growth, resistance to environmental conditions, and seasonal variation.

256. SMITH, D. C. "Experimental Studies of Lichen Physiology," *Symposia of the Society for General Microbiology, 13* (1963), 31–50.
  A review of the physiology of the fungal and algal symbionts of lichens.

257. SMITH, D. C. "Studies in the Physiology of Lichens. IV. Carbohydrates in *Peltigera polydactyla* and the Utilization of Absorbed Glucose," *New Phytologist, 62* (1963), 205–216.

258. SMITH, D. C., and E. A. DREW. "Studies in the Physiology of Lichens. V. Translocation from the Algal Layer to the Medulla in *Peltigera polydactyla*." *New Phytologist, 64* (1965), 195–200.

259. SMYTH, E. S. "A Contribution to the Physiology and Ecology of *Peltigera canina* and *P. polydactyla*," *Ann. Botany*, 48 (1934), 781–818.

260. SÖDERBERG, U. "A Note on the Action of Usnic Acid on Anaesthetized Cats," *Acta Physiol. Scand.*, 28 (1953), 202–210.

261. STÅLFELT, M. G. "Über die Beziehung zwischen den Assimilations- und Atmungsgrössen," *Svensk Botan. Tidskr.*, 30 (1936), 343–354.

262. STÅLFELT, M. G. "Der Gasaustausch der Flechten," *Planta*, 29 (1939), 11–31.

263. STEINER, M. "Wachstums- und Entwicklungsphysiologie der Flechten." In *Handbuch der Pflanzenphysiologie* (W. Ruhland, ed.) (Berlin: Springer, 1964), 15, Part 1, 758–801.

264. STEVENS, R. B. "Morphology and Ontogeny of *Dermatocarpon aquaticum*," *Am. J. Botany*, 28 (1941), 59–69.
Contains drawings and a photograph that illustrate chromosomes, sexual structures, and various stages in the development of the reproductive structures.

265. STOCKER, O. "Physiologische und ökologische Untersuchungen an Laub- und Strauchflechten," *Flora* (Jena), 121 (1927), 334–415.

266. STOCKER, O. "Wasseraufnahme und Wasserspeicherung bei Thallophyten." In *Handbuch der Pflanzenphysiologie* (W. Ruhland, ed.) (Berlin: Springer, 1956), 3, 160–172.

267. STOLL, A., A. BRACK, and J. RENZ. "Die antibakterielle Wirkung der Usninsäure auf Mykobakterien und andere Mikroorganismen," *Experientia*, 3 (1947), 115–116.

268. SYRETT, P. J. "Nitrogen Assimilation." In *Physiology and Biochemistry of Algae* (R. A. Lewin, ed.) (New York: Academic Press, 1962), 171–188.

269. TALLIS, J. H. Lichens and Atmospheric Pollution. In "Recent Studies of Lichens," *Advan. Sci.* (British Assoc.) 31 (1964), 250–252.

270. THOMAS, E. A. "Die Spezifizität des Parietins als Flechtenstoff," *Ber. Schweiz. Botan. Ges.*, 45 (1936), 191–197.

271. THOMAS, E. A. "Über die Biologie von Flechtenbildnern," *Beitr. Kryptogamenflora Schweiz*, 9 (1939), 1–208.
An outstanding, detailed study of the biology of lichen symbionts. Describes the isolation and culture techniques for algal and fungal symbionts, their physiology, and the lichen substances formed by isolated lichen fungi. Describes lichen synthesis experiments beginning with the separate symbionts.

Contains six plates of photographs of mycobiont and phycobiont colonies, and artificially synthesized lichen structures.

272. Thomson, J. W. "Modern Species Concepts: Lichens," *Bryologist, 66* (1963), 94–100.

273. Tichý, V., and V. Rypáček. "The Influence of the Habitat on the Fungistatic Activity of the Lichens." (In Czechoslovakian with English summary). *Spisy Vydávané Přirodovědeckou Fakultou Masarykovy Univ., Publ. Fac. Sci. Univ. Masaryk, Rada, K9* (346): (1953), 101–118.

274. Tobler, F. *Biologie der Flechten* (Berlin: Borntraege, 1925), 265 pp.
An introduction to the cultural and physiological aspects of the lichen symbiosis.

275. Tobler, F. *Die Flechten* (Jena: Gustav Fischer, 1934), 85 pp.
A well-illustrated introduction to the biology of lichen symbioses with references and comments at the end of each of the four chapters.

276. Tobler, F. "Die Kultur von Flechten." In *Abderhaldens Handbuch der biologischen Arbeitsmethoden* (Berlin: Urban und Schwarzenberg, 12, 1939), 1491–1511.
Describes various techniques and materials for culturing lichen fungi, lichen algae, and the composite forms.

277. Tobler, F. "Die Flechtensymbiose als Wirkstoffrage. I. Die Keimung von Flechtensporen und ihre Anregung durch Wirkstoffe," *Planta, 34* (1944), 34–40.
A study of the influence of nutritional factors on the germination of spores of *Xanthoria parietina.*

278. Tomaselli, R. "Nuovo Contributo Alle Richerche Sulla Presenza di 'Fiscione' in Colture Pure di *Xanthoriomyces*," *Atti dell'Istituto Botanico e Laboratorio Crittogamico dell' Università di Pavia, 14* (1957), 1–18.

279. Tomaselli, R. "Gli Aminoacidi Come Fonte di Azoto Nella Crescita 'in vitro' di Micosimbionti Lichenici," *Atti dell'Istituto Botanico e Laboratorio Crittogamico dell' Università di Pavia, 16* (1959), 180–191.

280. Tomaselli, R., F. Luciani, and F. Furnari. "Sulla Presenza di Ificella-rioli e di Conidi in Micobionti Lichenici Coltivati 'in vitro,'" *Bollettino dell'Istituto di Botanica dell' Università di Catania, 4* (1963), 111–116.

281. Tschermak, E. "Untersuchungen über die Beziehungen von Pilz und Alge im Flechtenthallus," *Öster. Botan. Z., 90* (1941), 233–307.
Contains drawings and descriptions that illustrate different types of haustoria in many lichens. An excellent treatment of the physical relationships between lichenized algae and fungi.

282. TSCHERMAK, E. "Weitere Untersuchungen zur Frage des Zusammenlebens von Pilz und Alge in den Flechten," *Öster. Botan. Z.*, 92 (1943), 15–24.

283. ULLRICH, J. "Beobachtungen über die vegetative Verbreitung der Cladonien durch Thallusfragmente," *Ber. Deut. Botan. Ges.*, 67 (1954) 1955, 391–394.

284. VARTIA, K. O. "On Antibiotic Effects of Lichens and Lichen Substances." (Academic dissertation, Helsinki University, 1950 Helsinki, Finland).
Also published as Supplement No. 7 (1950) to *Annales Medicinae Experimentalis et Biologiae Fenniae.*
Includes a chapter on the medicinal uses of lichens.

285. VIRTANEN, O. E. "The Antibiotic Activity of Some Amino Compound Derivatives of L-Usnic Acid II," *Suomen Kemistilehti*, B 27 (1954), 67–70.

286. VIRTANEN, O. E. "Derivatives of Usnic Acid with the Most Important Tuberculostatic Agents," *Suomen Kemistilehti*, B 28 (1955), 125–126.

287. VIRTANEN, O. E., and O. E. KILPIÖ. "On the 'in vivo' Fungistatic Activity of an Usnic Acid Preparation With the Trade Name USNO," *Suomen Kemistilehti*, B 30 (1957), 8–9.

288. VOGEL, S. "Niedere 'Fensterpflanzen' in der südafrikanischen Wüste. Eine ökologische Schilderung," *Beitr. Biol. Pflanzen*, 31 (1955), 45–135.

289. WACHTMEISTER, C. A. "Identification of Lichen Acids by Paper Chromatography," *Botan. Not.*, 109 (1956), 313–324.

290. WACHTMEISTER, C. A. "Studies on the Chemistry of Lichens," *Svensk Kem. Tidskr.*, 70 (1958), 117–133.

291. WARÉN, H. "Reinkulturen von Flechtengonidien," *Övfers. Finska Vetenskaps-Soc. Förhand.*, 61 (1918–1919), 1–79.
An outstanding study on the axenic culture of lichen algae. Presents a historical review of investigations on the culture of lichen algae. Describes the isolation and culture techniques of lichen algae, particularly *Trebouxia*, and their utilization of different nitrogen sources. Includes descriptions of the cytology, development, and cultural morphology of these phycobionts. Contains one plate of drawings and eight plates of photographs that illustrate cellular details of phycobionts, their colonies on agar media, and their growth on agar media with different nitrogen sources.

292. WATANABE, A., and T. KIYOHARA. "Symbiotic Blue-Green Algae of Lichens, Liverworts and Cycads," *Plant and Cell Physiology* (Special Issue: "Studies on Microalgae and Photosynthetic Bacteria") (1963), 189–196.

Describes a procedure used to isolate the blue-green (*Nostoc*) phycobionts of several *Peltigera* species into axenic cultures.

293. WATSON, D. G., W. C. HANSON, and J. J. DAVIS. "Strontium-90 in Plants and Animals of Arctic Alaska, 1959–61," *Science, 144* (1964), 1005–1009.

294. WEBER, W. A. "Environmental Modification and the Taxonomy of the Crustose Lichens," *Svensk Botan. Tidskr., 56* (1962), 293–333.
An excellent account of the different types of environmental modifications found in crustose lichens, with special reference to *Acarospora*. The article is illustrated with one color plate. The author discusses some of the taxonomic problems and difficulties in lichenology.

295. WERNER, R. G. "Sur la Multiplication par Conidies dans les Cultures Pures des Champignons de Lichens," *Compt. Rend. Congr. Soc. Savantes* (1926), 113–115.

296. WERNER, R. G. "Recherches Biologiques et Expérimentales sur les Ascomycètes de Lichens." (Doctoral dissertation, University of Paris, 1927.)

297. WERNER, R. G. "Cultures Pures des Champignons des Lichens Incrustants," *Bull. Soc. Hist. Nat. d'Afrique du Nord, 25* (1934), 130–137.

298. WHELAN, W. J. "Starch, Glycogen, Fructosans and Similar Polysaccharides." In *Modern Methods of Plant Analysis* (K. Paech, and M. V. Tracey, eds.) (Berlin: Springer, 1955), 2, 145–196.

299. WILHELMSEN, J. B. "Chlorophylls in the Lichens *Peltigera, Parmelia,* and *Xanthoria*," *Botan. Tidsskr., 55* (1959), 30–36.

300. YAMAZAKI, M., M. MATSUO, and S. SHIBATA. "Biosynthesis of Lichen Depsides, Lecanoric Acid and Atranorin," *Chem. Pharm. Bull., 13* (1965), 1015–1017.

301. YAMAZAKI, M., and S. SHIBATA. "Biosynthesis of Lichen Substances. II. Participation of C_1-Unit to the Formation of Beta-Orcinol Type Lichen Depside," *Chem. Pharm. Bull., 14* (1966), 96–97.

302. ZEHNDER, A. "Über den Einfluss von Wuchsstoffen auf Flechtenbildner," *Ber. Schweiz. Botan. Ges., 59* (1949), 201–267.
Influence of growth factors on lichen algae, mostly *Trebouxia*, and lichen fungi.

303. ZEHNDER, A. "Über den Einfluss antibiotischer Stoffe auf das Wachstum von Grünalgen," *Experientia, 7* (1951), 100.

304. ZEITLER, I. "Untersuchungen über die Morphologie, Entwicklungsgeschichte und Systematik von Flechtengonidien," *Öster. Botan. Z., 101* (1954), 453–487.

Index

149